Elaine Farrell is a freelance researcher and writer with an NHS background. She has worked alongside NHS mental health services for the past four years and is currently training as a mental health nurse with the East Sussex and West Kent Institute of Nursing at Sussex University.

Elaine Farrell is author of *Choices in Health Care* (Optima 1989), and *Mental Health: A Survival Guide* is her second book.

GW00384911

MENTAL HEALTH
A Survival Guide

ELAINE FARRELL

An OPTIMA book

First published in 1991 by
Macdonald Optima, a division of
Macdonald & Co. (Publishers) Ltd

A member of Maxwell Macmillan Pergamon Publishing Corporation

British Library Cataloguing in Publication Data
Farrell, Elaine
    The mental health survival guide.
    1. Man. Mental health
    I. Title
    613

    ISBN 0-356-14021-0

Macdonald & Co. (Publishers) Ltd
Orbit House
1 New Fetter Lane
London EC4A 1AR

Typeset in Century Schoolbook by
Leaper & Gard Ltd, Bristol, England

Printed and bound in Great Britain by
The Guernsey Press Co. Ltd, Guernsey, Channel Islands.

To John

'I cannot give the reasons
I only sing the tunes
The sadness of the seasons
The madness of the moons'

Mervyn Peake

CONTENTS

INTRODUCTION   xiii

1 MAD, BAD OR JUST PLAIN SAD?   1
  How mental distress is classified   3
    Neurosis   3
    Psychosis   3
    Personality disorder   4
  Possible causes of mental distress   4
  Madness as a label   5
  Categories of mental distress   7
    Agoraphobia   8
    Alcohol dependence   11
    Alzheimer's disease   13
    Anorexia nervosa and secondary anorexia   13
    Anxiety   14
    Autism   15
    Bulimia nervosa   16
    Dementia/deterioration of the brain   17
    Depression   18
    Drug dependence   26
    Huntington's chorea   30
    Hyperactivity   30
    Hypochondria   31
    Hysteria   31
    Mania   32
    Manic depression   33
    Obsessive disorders   34
    Paranoia   36
    Parkinson's disease   37
    Phobias   38
    Sociopathic (psychopathic) disorder   38
    Schizophrenia   39
  Useful addresses   44

2 YOU KNOW WHAT YOUR PROBLEM IS,
   DON'T YOU!   47
   Mental health   50
   Understanding stress   51
   Stress and you   53
     Possible signs of stress   54
   Causes of stress   55
     Who is most at risk from stress?   57
   Dealing with stress   59
     Looking at the way you breathe   60
     Relaxation exercises   61
     Self-hypnosis   63
     Massage   64
     Meditation   65
     Yoga   66
     Exercise   66
   Dealing with tension   66
   Measuring your self-esteem   68
     Improving your self-esteem   71
     Dealing with criticism   72
   Assertiveness   74
     Assertive rights   74

3 HEALTHY BODIES, HEALTHY MINDS   76
   Alcohol   76
     Knowing how much you drink   77
     How much should you drink?   79
   Diet   79
     Self-regulation of eating   81
     What might help   82
   Exercise   83
     Safety   84
     Suitability and satisfaction   85
     Suppleness, stamina and strength   85
     Motivation   86
   Getting a good night's sleep   87
   Staying well   88

4 GROWING GOOD? — A GUIDE TO THERAPY   89
    Choosing therapy   91
    The psychotherapies   93
        Counselling   93
        Psychoanalysis   94
        Psychoanalytic psychotherapy   96
        Neo-Freudian analysis   96
        Jungian psychotherapy   96
        Post-analytic one-to-one therapies   97
        Behavioural and cognitive behaviour therapies   97
        Group therapy   102
        Family therapy   103
        Marital therapy   104
        Sex therapy and psycho-sexual counselling   105
        Self-help groups   105
        Art therapy   106
    Availability of therapy   107
    Useful addresses   110

5 SURVIVING COMMUNITY CARE   114
    Finding support   116
    Accommodation   116
    Employment   120
    Getting to know people   121
    Health care services   122
        Acute hospital care   122
        Day hospitals   124
        Mental health centres   124
    Mental health care professionals   124
        GP (general practitioner)   125
        Mental health (psychiatric) nurse   125
        Psychiatrist   126
        Clinical psychologist   126
        Mental health social worker   127
        Occupational therapist   127
        Art therapist   127
        Industrial therapist   127
    Useful addresses   128

6 MENTAL HEALTH AND HUMAN RIGHTS 130
The patients' charter 131
Mental Health Act 1983 132
Legal rights under the Mental Health Act 1983 133
Admission to and discharge from a hospital for
people with acute or chronic mental health
problems 134
Compulsory admission from patient's home 135
Consent to treatment 137
Sections 128 and 134 141
Mental Health Review Tribunals 142
The mental health consumer movement 142
Patients' councils 143
The role of advocacy in achieving mental health
rights 143
Useful addresses 145

7 DRUG TREATMENTS AND THEIR
ALTERNATIVES 148
The need for drugs 148
Tranquillisers 150
Major tranquillisers 150
Minor tranquillisers 151
Drugs and their side effects 151
Major tranquillisers 152
Antidepressant drugs 153
Minor tranquillisers 155
Lithium treatment and its side-effects 155
Electroplexy 156
Alternative or complementary treatments 157
Acupuncture 157
Alexander technique 158
Anthroposophical medicine 158
Applied kinesiology 158
Aromatherapy 159
Art therapy 159
Bach Flower Remedies 159
Colour therapy 162
Dance therapy 162

Herbalism 163
Hydrotherapy 164
Ionisation therapy 164
Massage 165
Music therapy 165
Reflexology 165
Rolfing 166
Shiatsu/acupressure 167
T'ai chi 167
Useful addresses 168

INDEX 171

INTRODUCTION

Mental distress is something that happens to someone else. And when it does, someone else deals with it. Well, perhaps that is what many of us like to think, but in fact it's a long way from the truth, as the following evidence demonstrates:

— one in four people suffer from some form of mental distress such as depression, anxiety, phobias, psychotic symptoms or an inability to cope with life's pressures.

— an estimated one in ten recently delivered mothers will experience post-natal depression;

— a possible one in 1,000 newly delivered mothers experience a post-partum (after the birth) psychotic illness;

— one in ten people experience depression at some time in their lives and this is a particularly likely response to a major loss such as bereavement or at times of life change such as adolescence or retirement;

— obsessive compulsive disorders, such as constant hand-washing or ritual performance, are experienced by up to 4.6 per cent of people coming into contact with the mental health services;

— an estimated 2 per cent of the population over the age of 15 are likely to have significant problems with alcohol dependence. Twenty per cent of admissions to mental health hospitals in Scotland are through alcoholism;

— the average risk of developing a schizophrenic type disorder is around 8 people in 1,000;

— one person out of every 200 will develop mania at some time in their lives;

— In 1986 there were 197,251 admissions to psychiatric hospitals.

In addition to these figures are the people who never come to the attention of mental health services and are therefore not recorded. They tend to try and cope by themselves or with the support of relatives. Statistics show that the major reason for seeing a family doctor is emotional rather than physical, including requests for sleeping pills, iron tablets and tonics and antidepressants.

All this goes to show that people who do not experience some form of mental distress at some time in their lives are probably fairly unusual and certainly very lucky. Or perhaps they are very skilled at avoiding situations that detract from their mental well-being, in which case they have no need to read further.

This book has been written to help the effort to promote our mental health survival by removing some of the fear and ignorance that surrounds mental distress by promoting skills needed to deal with some of the factors that contribute to mental distress, including stress and lack of physical well-being; by examining various treatments and therapies that are currently used in the care of mental distress; by providing some knowledge and understanding of the different types of mental health services that are available and by promoting the understanding of and fight for the rights of mental health service users.

1
MAD, BAD OR JUST PLAIN SAD?

We all carry within us the seeds of our own mental health problems. There is no point looking at those who suffer severe forms of mental distress and seeing them as 'different'. They are not. It is only that they have been subjected to an environment that has allowed their seeds to flourish. Harsh, critical, unaffectionate parents, doting, demanding parents, complicated family relationships, poor nutrition, poverty, unemployment, too little success, too much success, unhelpful coping strategies — all these things and more can destroy our mental well-being. And in the same way as a cactus will not flourish in a rain forest nor a rose in the desert, so some people will not flourish in the environments within which they find themselves.

It may be, of course, that the seeds of mental health problems are stronger and more vigorous in some than others, but there is still evidence that given an environment that nurtures that individual as a whole, rather than the seed of mental distress, many of those at risk from severe mental distress may be spared. Making a hard and fast distinction, then, between the mentally 'well' and the mentally 'ill' is artificial, although it has traditionally made the mentally 'well' feel more comfortable, as well as providing some form of care for the mentally 'ill'.

We all experience 'madness' at some times during our lives. Too much to drink at a party can make us behave so 'out of character' that we prefer to forget our behaviour, or we blame it on the alcohol, rather than admit to ourselves that the alcohol merely removed our normal inhibitions and allowed something of ourselves, something we might ordinarily prefer to keep hidden, out. It might have been self-pity, aggression or lust. It might have made us talk rubbish, fall over or embarrass all around us. However, once the effects of the alcohol have passed, we regain our self-control.

Alcohol causes a change in the bio-chemical balance of our brains and bodies. Our vision and speech slur, we lose co-ordination, our reflexes are retarded, our behaviour is affected. But as long as we are not too embarrassing and don't damage other people or their property, the loss of control through alcohol is accepted, even encouraged, by those around us. However, if something affects our body, brain or mind and this results in bizarre behaviour that others do not understand and the causes of which are not known, then there is far less tolerance. We want the authorities to step in. We want 'mad' people locked away. Losing control, whether in the form of a spectacular psychosis or a gradually dawning depression, is usually regarded as undesirable.

For some people the loss of control is very severe and very distressing, to themselves and to others. To hear people saying bad things about you when there is no-one around (auditory hallucinations) or to feel that your mind is being controlled is not something that any of us would choose to experience, but for some people it is a reality. We do not really understand why. But then we do not understand how many medications work, even though we know they do and we accept that they do every time we take them for some ailment.

Some people learn to live with their symptoms and with support and/or medication are able to live their lives as they would wish. However, for many others the onset or repetition of their symptoms means that they are less able to cope with many of the demands of everyday life, and the fear and prejudice that surrounds their disorder means that they lose out on support.

Understanding something about the different ways in which mental distress expresses itself can help the sufferer and cut down on a great deal of prejudice.

HOW MENTAL DISTRESS IS CLASSIFIED

The main experiences of mental distress are given clinical classifications or labels. These fall into three main groups: neuroses, psychoses and personality disorders.

Neurosis

Mental health problems deemed to be neurotic in nature are those characterised by excessive unhappiness, unhealthy levels of anxiety and unhelpful, perhaps even destructive, ways of behaving (referred to as maladaptive). There is no loss of contact with reality and people usually know that something is wrong.

The main ways in which a neurosis will show itself is through anxiety, depression or obsessive/compulsive behaviour, although this in itself is usually an expression of an unbearably high level of anxiety. Psychosomatic or hysterical illnesses (such as hysterical blindness) also fall into this category. As the definitions of different categories of mental distress further on in this chapter show, mental health problems of a neurotic nature are experienced as exaggerations of normal thoughts and reactions.

Psychosis

A psychosis is usually signified by a loss of contact with reality, although the sufferer may often have more insight than they are given credit for. The person may well not know there is anything wrong with them. They may hold fixed false beliefs, thinking themselves to be very rich, very powerful or even someone else. They may experience hallucinations. It is often the loss of contact with reality (usually temporary), plus the distorted perception (eg hearing voices, believing the mind to be controlled by others) that is so frightening for most people.

A psychotic episode can be triggered by drugs, alcohol or other toxins in the body. It can be triggered by lack of sleep, a metabolic disorder or infection. This is known as an organic psychosis, toxic confusional state, acute brain failure or even an acute delirious reaction. However, a psychotic experience can often happen with no known cause (though stress is often implicated) and, depending on the nature of the experience, a person might be diagnosed as suffering from schizophrenia, manic depression or endogenous (psychotic) depression.

Personality disorder

The common term for people who have a personality disorder is psychopath, although with the emphasis on the causes of mental distress originating from society, the term sociopath is gaining popularity.

A sociopath or psychopath is a person who does not experience guilt or remorse at their actions that may cause pain to others. They are often impervious to punishment. They do not learn from experience. It is their character that appears to be damaged or disordered as opposed to their thoughts or moods. They have quite often (but not always) experienced a distressing or disturbed upbringing.

It is people in this small category of mental disorder that create much of the prejudice against others who may have been in hospital with some form of mental health problem but who would be most unlikely to hurt someone else, even if provoked. People with a personality disorder may or may not experience other forms of mental distress.

POSSIBLE CAUSES OF MENTAL DISTRESS

In reality when people experience mental distress to the extent that they need care, it is often very difficult to get at the root of their experience. Consequently what may appear to be a clear cut category on paper is far more complicated in experience, despite what might be claimed by 'experts' such as psychiatrists.

The causes of mental distress are complex and the most likely explanation is that several factors (physical, psychological and social) combine to cause problems.

Over the years there have been a range of opinions, some emphasising physical explanations (particularly heredity) and some emphasising the effects of the environment.

There is a belief that while most neuroses are determined by the environment (eg cultural influences on women), mental distress that is psychotic in nature arises when an inherited potential is triggered by environmental stresses. However, there is no reason to suppose that a neurotic tendency is not inherited in the same way.

It is often suggested that genetic factors make some people more susceptible to mental health problems. However, it is the susceptibility and not the problem itself that is passed on. Stress is seen as a crucial factor in the development of mental health problems.

The 'medical model' view of psychiatry emphasises physical causes (eg heredity and its biochemical expression) and treatments, while the 'social model' emphasises environmental determinants and stresses psychological treatments.

Mental health problems of any kind can severely affect someone's ability to live a fulfilling life, particularly in a society that values achievement, success, gain, status and wealth.

MADNESS AS A LABEL

When I was very small I had a friend from whom I was inseparable. He came everywhere with me. On the bus when I went shopping with my mother. To the dinner table when we were at home. Out to play with my friends. His name was Roy Rogers and he was a cowboy. He also appeared to be invisible to other people and so getting a seat for him was sometimes difficult, but on the whole, we managed.

This fantasy, or delusion, was tolerated, because inconvenient as it often proved to be, it was quite 'normal' for a 3-year-old to have a pretend friend. However, when an adult has a fantasy and, like the 3-year-old, cannot distinguish it from reality, then they may be labelled mentally ill, schizophrenic or mad.

Working in the mental health services, I am often struck by the way psychiatric 'labels' are used. For instance, it is not uncommon for a nurse or a doctor to refer to a patient as 'agitated depressed' or 'paranoid schizophrenic' as a shorthand to describe the type of symptoms the patient experiences. And so on ward rounds, or nursing shift handovers, the introduction to the update of a patient's well-being might well start: 'John Smith, 57, agitated depressed'. More disturbing is when a professional refers to a patient as a 'typical old schizy' or 'chronic schiz'. But saddest of all are the patients who 'become' their illness. 'I'm a manic-depressive', one patient told me. I felt saddened by her description of herself. No longer was she a mother, an employee or simply a nice person. Her 'illness' was her identity. She was a manic-depressive. The reasons why people adopt a sick role are complex. Being ill is an acceptable reason for being unable to do many of the things that are expected of us. But for many people who come into contact with mental health services, illness becomes an identity because of the way patients are labelled by the staff. It may well have been that this lady had adopted the sick role as a way of defining herself as a person. But there were forces that reinforced this self-image. Her son, a clinical psychologist, wrote long letters to her consultant psychiatrist discussing his mother's case. His letters to his mother were filled with references to her illness, although little sign of affection showed through. It was as if the only important part of her identity was her illness; that was the way she gained some sense of significance. Diagnosing somebody as suffering from a specific mental health problem can therefore have a variety of effects, some intended and some not:

— it ensures that they will get care;

— it can provide a legitimate reason why someone may be unable to cope;

— it can make them seem different to others;

— it can stigmatize and socially disadvantage them.

CATEGORIES OF MENTAL DISTRESS

Whatever the advantages and disadvantages of being diagnosed or labelled through some form of mental distress, it is a system that exists and for that reason this chapter includes these categories with a brief explanation of what they are, their signs and symptoms, possible causes and likely treatments. Some of these categories or 'labels' will be familiar to you. Many have become part of our everyday language: for example, 'I'm depressed' is a popular substitute for 'I'm fed up' or 'I'm unhappy'. 'He's paranoid' or 'She's a hypochondriac' are not uncommon sayings. And usually they are seen as being pretty harmless. Some expressions are quite coy; 'I'm bad with my nerves' is far more acceptable to many people than 'I am mentally ill'.

The categories given here are medical or clinical classifications of mental health problems. They are designed to describe a cluster of symptoms as a form of shorthand for mental health professionals. However, like many other forms of classification, clinical classifications of mental health problems or, as they are more readily called, mental illnesses, tend to end up classifying not symptoms but people themselves. And until mental illness as a medical description goes out of fashion this danger will continue to exist.

It is very tempting to be a total heretic and avoid all classifications. However, to an extent this would render this book less useful and even impractical because it would be ignoring a state that exists and an experience that people have. To avoid referring to schizophrenia as a term describing a form of mental distress because of the lack of knowledge that exists about its causes, and because no two schizophrenic experiences are alike, is living in cloud cuckoo land. Some of the people who read this book may have been labelled as 'schizophrenic', something that is treated by the medical profession as a lifelong condition. Others may have friends or relatives who suffer from symptoms of schizophrenia and will need to use the classification as a point of reference. And most will have seen the

7

term used by the media, usually wrongly. For readers who have little or no understanding of mental health problems, gaining insight into the use and abuse of terms and a greater understanding of the problems in a way that rids them of fear and ignorance is of just as much importance. And so, with some reluctance, the classifications stay. However the emphasis is on breaking down the barriers between 'well' and 'ill' rather than reinforcing them.

A note of caution must be introduced here. I once read a book about depression from cover to cover, and at the end of it I decided that I must have been depressed for my entire life! Such is the danger of reading anything that describes mental health problems, because the symptoms are often exaggerations of feelings and experiences we have all had at some time to varying degrees. Also, many of the symptoms experienced during a psychotic illness are grounded in reality, but a reality which is seriously skewed.

For people who want to know more about particular problems, a list of useful organisations is given at the end of this chapter.

Agoraphobia

A phobia is an exaggerated fear. Perhaps the two most well-known phobias are claustrophobia (fear of confined spaces) and agoraphobia.

Agoraphobia is usually seen as a fear of open spaces or the fear of going outdoors, perhaps just the opposite of claustrophobia. However, it is slightly more complicated than this. Agoraphobia is perhaps described more accurately as a fear of public places, particularly where return to a safe familiar place is difficult. Consequently some enclosed places, like busy shopping arcades, can also trigger attacks.

The onset of agoraphobia may be experienced as a panic attack in a particular shop or venue. This panic attack is so unpleasant that the sufferer will then try to avoid that particular setting. However, because the fear is, in reality, most probably linked to something other than the setting in which the attack takes place, the avoidance of the setting does not prevent the panic attacks. These continue to be experienced when the sufferer has to go to the corner of the street to post a letter, into the garden to empty rubbish into the dustbin and eventually even when the sufferer tries to leave the house.

Signs and symptoms   Feelings of anxiety when leaving the home which may culminate in a panic attack. Sufferers may feel terrified, be unable to think straight, their breathing will be affected as when extremely nervous, they may break out in a cold sweat, experience palpitations and feel that they are at extreme risk from some unknown source.

Possible causes   The phobia may well be a response to some underlying anxiety with which the patient is not in touch, or is unable to confront.

What might help   Behaviour therapy is seen as being the most effective approach to dealing with this problem. It is undertaken in an individual or group setting (ie a group of people who share or have shared the same experience). Behaviour therapy concentrates on the symptoms rather than the underlying cause (see Chapter 6), although counselling and psychotherapy can be used in some instances. Learning relaxation in conjunction with another approach may be useful. There are also self-help programmes available and more information can be gained about these from the Phobics Society (see Useful Addresses below).

Some of the many possible phobias

Animals	—	Zoophobia
Bacteria	—	Bacteriaphobia or microphobia
Bees	—	Apiphobia or mellissophobia
Being afraid	—	Phobophobia
Being alone	—	Autophobia or monophobia
Being buried alive	—	Taphophobia
Being stared at	—	Scopophobia

Birds	—	Ornithophobia
Blood	—	Haematophobia
Blushing	—	Erythrophobia
Cancer	—	Cancerophobia
Cats	—	Ailurophobia
Childbirth	—	Tocophobia
Corpses	—	Necrophobia
Crowds	—	Ochlophobia
Darkness	—	Nyctophobia
Death	—	Thanatophobia
Dirt	—	Mysophobia
Disease	—	Pathophobia
Dogs	—	Cynophobia
Dreams	—	Oneirophobia
Enclosed spaces	—	Claustrophobia
Fire	—	Pyrophobia
Flying	—	Aerophobia
Foreigners or strangers	—	Xenophobia
Heart disease	—	Cardiophobia
Heights	—	Acrophobia
Horses	—	Hippophobia
Illness	—	Nosophobia
Insanity	—	Lyssophobia
Insects	—	Entomophobia
Light	—	Photophobia
Lightning	—	Astrapophobia
Marriage	—	Gamophobia
Pain	—	Algophobia
Reptiles	—	Batrachophobia
Ridicule	—	Katagelophobia
Satan	—	Satanophobia
Sexual intercourse	—	Coitophobia
Sharp objects	—	Belenophobia
Sleep	—	Hypnophobia
Speed	—	Tachophobia
Spiders	—	Arachnophobia
Thunder	—	Keraunophobia
Travel	—	Hodophobia
Venereal disease	—	Venerophobia

Water   —   Hydrophobia
Women   —   Gynophobia
Worms   —   Helminthophobia

Alcohol dependence

Most people would throw up their hands in horror if you suggested to them that they might use and abuse drugs, and yet they would be quite happy to down a few pints, gin and tonics or glasses of wine, often several times a week and with no fear of the consequences, although there may be some short-term repentance and seeing of light during a severe hangover. Within our culture, people who do not drink alcohol are seen as distinctly odd. These poor souls are generally ridiculed and badgered for making everyone else feel bad in some perverse way (for some reason alcohol consumption as a form of self-harm is more securely carried out in groups).

Our culture is in fact highly tolerant of alcohol abuse: tolerant that is until the abuser loses his or her entertainment value and becomes a nuisance or out of control, in which case the tolerance ends abruptly and other attitudes come quickly to the fore. Sufferers then find themselves without jobs, friends or family and often in the hands of the psychiatric or prison services.

Alcohol dependence sneaks up on people because of its innocent image, and yet the psychological and physical damage it can cause people from all backgrounds (alcohol doesn't discriminate — it takes victims from all walks of life) can be devastating and permanent. Alcohol dependence is not solely caused through consumption of spirits. Any alcoholic beverage can cause dependence including beer, wine and cider. It is the alcohol that does the damage, not the form it comes in. Alcohol dependence can cause depression, psychotic episodes including auditory and visual hallucinations. It can cause extreme feelings of paranoia and even in some cases dementia through damage to the brain. All this is in addition to the physical damage alcohol consumption can cause to the body.

Signs and symptoms Increased consumption of alcohol of any kind, particularly if associated with the feeling of a need for a drink. Signs and symptoms grow with the level of dependence and may include memory blackouts, mood changes, impaired thinking and concentration, breakdown of relationships, neglect of self and in the long term hallucinations and trembling can occur.

High levels of alcohol consumption cause widespread damage to the body, burning through the stomach lining causing ulceration, and inflaming the liver to the point where it cannot regenerate itself. Severe liver damage (cirrhosis) is fatal.

Possible causes As with many other mental health problems, the causes can be explained as being physical, (ie some individuals are more prone because of some inborn predisposition), psychological or social (alcoholism is a greater problem within cultures where drinking is culturally reinforced, such as the north-east of England and in Scotland).

What might help Depending on the severity of the problem, a person might need detoxification in hospital (treatment with drugs to neutralise the very distressing symptoms of withdrawal), followed by some form of therapy. There are a number of support groups of which Alcoholics Anonymous is probably the most well-known. (Address of nearest branch will be given in the telephone directory.) Alcohol Concern is another national organisation with local branches. In the London area ACCEPT is an organisation that offers free therapy services. There are also private clinics for those that can afford them. To find out about these contact Alcohol Concern.

Alzheimer's disease
See **Dementia**

Anorexia nervosa and secondary anorexia

Anorexia nervosa has been much publicised in recent years. More likely to affect young women (under 25) than men, this illness is closely linked with the sufferer's self-esteem. Someone suffering from anorexia will be obsessed with weight loss and although they may be fascinated by food they will go to extreme lengths to avoid eating.

Secondary anorexia is slightly different in signs and symptoms and while someone who has anorexia nervosa may appear to have a lot of energy and vitality despite their debilitated condition, someone suffering from secondary anorexia will show many of the signs of depression. The cause may well be anger turning to self-starvation as a way of taking control of one's life and getting back at those who have caused hurt.

Signs and symptoms   Marked weight loss, bones showing under the skin which is dry and papery, sometimes with the growth of a fine downy hair on legs, arms and trunk. Blood pressure drops and the person will feel very cold. In women, the main sufferers, their monthly period will stop eventually. They may go to extreme lengths to avoid eating food, including hiding it about their person.

Possible causes   Anorexia is believed to be a response to underlying anxieties and misery in relation to life issues such as sexual and other relationships, examinations and work pressure. Because self-inflicted starvation prevents the development of womanhood (by reducing libido, stopping periods and producing a childish, waif-like figure) the emphasis on sexual issues is often focused upon although people who have spoken about their anorexia give a rounder picture and talk of their need to take control of their lives in the only way they can.

What might help   Anorexia is a very difficult condition to help as often the person's will is so strong it is really only their decision to change that can bring about any improvement. Many treatments have been tried (and are still tried) with little or no effect (for example electroplexy and hypnosis). A behaviour modification programme (where patients are rewarded for meals eaten or weight gained) appears to be most effective to date. However it is distressing for staff and patient alike. Sometimes such a programme is supported with drug treatment, sometimes not. However, at the end of the day, it comes down to the patient's decision to direct her incredible will towards getting well rather than towards self-starvation. If the major stimulus for the anorexia is seen to be originating from the family situation, then family therapy might be appropriate. Group and individual psychotherapy may well be offered by mental health professionals within the NHS. Private therapy is offered by Anorexia Anonymous.

Support may be very important, as people suffering from anorexia find that professional workers and others find it difficult to understand their situation. Anorexic Aid is a network of self-help groups set up and run by people who have experienced and recovered from anorexia or bulimia (see below).

Family support can be offered by Anorexic Family Aid in the form of advice and counselling.

Anxiety

Anxiety is something we all experience at certain times, such as when we have an interview for a job, have to sit an exam or perhaps speak in public. It is a high state of physical and mental arousal that enables us to cope with a situation we find threatening or particularly stressful. However, for someone suffering from anxiety or as it is sometimes known, a generalized anxiety disorder, the symptoms of anxiety are experienced to an unbearable degree all or most of the time, even when there is no situation of a particularly threatening nature. This results in an inability to relax when awake or sleep and creates an almost intolerable level of mental and physical agitation.

Signs and symptoms   Tension causing aches and pains, dry mouth, sweaty hands, diarrhoea, pounding heart, mind in turmoil worrying about things in a way which is out of proportion to the actual problem, difficulty in getting to sleep. Other symptoms include agitation, wringing of hands, constantly talking about matters that are causing concern. There may well be a fixation with possible accidents, becoming ill or failure. Acute anxiety may be experienced as a panic attack.

Anxiety often accompanies or underlies mental distress of various natures.

Possible causes   Anxiety is usually caused by unresolved tensions. Explanations as to how these tensions arise vary depending on different schools of thoughts. However, as with any other form of mental health problem each individual's experience will be unique.

What might help   Extreme anxiety may need some form of drug treatment as a temporary measure, but this is in no way a solution. Counselling psychotherapy can help by working towards an understanding of the causes of the anxiety and by developing ways of dealing with the experience. Equally, learning relaxation skills may help sufferers cope with their unpleasant symptoms or prevent panic attacks. Hypnotherapy is an approach that both induces deep relaxation and helps a person to explore the underlying cause of the anxiety. All of these approaches are used in the NHS and your GP may well be helpful in directing or referring you to the appropriate service, eg community psychiatric nurse or clinical psychologist. Private therapists advertise in health magazines.

Autism
Autism is characterised by a withdrawal from reality, a non-response to external stimuli, and a preoccupation with one's thoughts and fantasies. Autism is most commonly associated with children.

Signs and symptoms   The autistic child avoids eye contact or shows no desire to be picked up or cuddled. They are aware only of themselves much of the time and may lie motionless for hours. They may also be very aggressive, hitting out and screaming, but be unable to communicate through speech. Rituals are very important and there is often a high need for order, with personal belongings put carefully in exactly the same place or in the same direction.

Possible causes   The causes of autism are not known. However the belief that faulty parenting might be at the root of autism is no longer accepted.

What might help   Treatment tends to concentrate on ways of dealing with the behaviour presented by the children, particularly if that behaviour is noisy or aggressive. There is interest at present in the type of therapy that floods the child with the kinds of contact he or she usually tries to avoid, such as eye contact and close physical contact.

Information can be supplied by the National Autistic Society.

Bulimia nervosa

Bulimia is similar to anorexia nervosa in that sufferers hold a deep fear of becoming or being fat. However, their behaviour differs in as much as they are unable to starve themselves, indeed often 'binge', gorge themselves on food, and then make themselves sick or swallow quantities of laxatives in an attempt to purge themselves.

Signs and symptoms   Similar to those experienced by someone with anorexia except that people suffering from bulimia tend to have greater insight into what is happening to them. 'Bingeing' may often take place when others are not around.

Possible causes   The root causes of bulimia are believed to be similar to those for anorexia (see pp. 13–14).

What might help   As for anorexia.

Dementia/deterioration of the brain

The terms 'dementing' or 'senile' are increasingly being regarded as derogatory terms that assign sufferers to a 'no hope' category of care. Alternatives such as brain failure or deterioration are not attractive, but do at least attempt to break with stereotyping.

There are several different types of chronic physical deterioration of the brain, all of which are characterised by physical changes in the brain, that is, damage caused by disease. In dementia this deterioration or damage is irreversible.

Huntington's chorea and Alzheimer's disease are forms of mental disorder through physical deterioration of the brain itself.

Signs and symptoms   Marked memory and skill loss are the main signs of dementia or brain deterioration. There may also be a change in personality so that some qualities become lost while others become exaggerated. During the early stage of the onset of dementia, there is often a realisation of what is happening and this can in turn lead to other mental health problems such as depression. Anxiety and paranoia can also be experienced.

This type of mental health problem is extremely distressing for the sufferer and relatives and friends. There is no cure for brain deterioration and so it is essential that sufferers' dignity and well-being is maintained with the help of professional and non-professional carers.

Possible causes   With Alzheimer's disease the brain experiences a physical change. Nerve endings deteriorate and there is a loss of neurotransmitters or chemical 'messengers'. There appears to be some link between the absorption of aluminium into the body's system and brain deterioration.

With other types of dementia damage is caused by restricted blood flow causing brain cells to die. Strokes are one cause of brain deterioration.

What might help As has been pointed out brain deterioration is irreversible and so the emphasis has to be on quality of life. At present there still seems to be an emphasis on longevity and quality of life comes in a poor second. This has resulted in very negative attitudes on the part of many professional carers, to the extent that sufferers only receive essential care such as feeding and toileting. This attitude is changing. Physiotherapy, reminiscence therapy (short-term memory deteriorates before long-term memory), reality orientation, occupational therapy and speech therapy are all important to the person who is suffering from any form of dementia. This approach helps them maintain and enjoy as many of their diminishing faculties as possible.

Depression

Many of us will have experienced depression to some degree. It appears that women are twice as likely to be affected than men, although it may well be that men show their depression in different ways (such as turning to alcohol).

Depression makes us feel miserable, saps our energy, makes us feel worthless, hopeless and even despairing. These low moods may pass after a few days or weeks. However, they can sometimes take a hold and despite all the urging to 'snap out of it' by friends and relatives some people can find themselves sinking deeper and deeper into depression, to a point where they may need professional help to sort themselves out.

Depression is often brought about as a reaction to a significant loss, such as the death of a loved one, the loss of a job, failing exams, the breakup of a marriage, even the loss of a limb through an accident or illness. It seems that when such a major loss happens to us we lose a great deal more than appears on the surface. We can lose our identity (as someone's wife, or husband) or prestige and self-esteem (as successful business person or member of the community) or even our sameness with other people (by losing a limb and becoming 'crippled' within a society that favours 'whole' people). This type of depression is known as re-active depression, ie depression brought about in response to an external event.

Sometimes, however, depression can arise without there being any apparent external event. This is known as endogenous (coming from within) depression. It is also referred to as psychotic depression if there are symptoms that are psychotic in nature. With endogenous depression there is an emphasis on genetic and biochemical factors, with the environment being the stimulus that triggers an episode. Less common than reactive depression, endoge-nous depression can be particularly distressing as suffer-ers find it hard to pin the causes on anything concrete such as a bereavement, and may also experience hallucin-ations.

Prevention strategies, including self-awareness and self-care, are particularly important for people who experience bouts of endogenous depression.

Signs and symptoms Someone who is depressed will experience a number of symptoms; they may feel very guilty over minor matters; they may feel miserable, hope-less; they may feel that they have failed in the past, whether or not this is a realistic perception. Outward signs will include slowness of pace when walking, a tendency to want to stay in bed, lowered head and drooping shoulders. A depressed person may want to avoid others, even close friends and relatives. Their appetite will diminish and they will eat less.

One test that is sometimes used to assess depression is the **Beck Depression Inventory**, given below.

Read over the statements grouped with each letter, A–U.

Pick out the statement within each group that best describes the way you feel today, that is, right at this moment. Circle the number next to the statement that you have chosen in each group. If two or more statements in a group describe the way you feel equally well, circle each one. Be sure to read over all of the statements in each group before you decide on one.

A Sadness

0   I do not feel sad.

1   I feel blue or sad.

2a   I am blue or sad all the time and I can't snap out of it.

2b   I am so sad or unhappy that it is quite painful.

3   I am so sad or unhappy that I can't stand it.

B Pessimism

0   I am not particularly pessimistic or discouraged about the future.

1   I feel discouraged about the future.

2a   I feel I have nothing to look forward to.

2b   I feel that I won't ever get over my troubles.

3   I feel that the future is hopeless and that things cannot improve.

C Sense of failure

0   I do not feel like a failure.

1   I feel I have failed more than the average person.

2a   I feel I have accomplished very little that is worthwhile or that means anything.

2b   As I look back on my life all I can see is a lot of failures.

3   I feel a complete failure as a person (parent, husband, wife).

D Dissatisfaction

0   I am not particularly dissatisfied.

1a   I feel bored most of the time.

1b   I don't enjoy things the way I used to.

2   I don't get satisfaction out of anything anymore.

3   I am dissatisfied with everything.

E Guilt
0   I don't feel particularly guilty.
1   I feel bad or unworthy a good part of the time.
2a   I feel quite guilty.
2b   I feel bad or unworthy practically all the time now.
3   I feel as though I am very bad or worthless.

F Expectation of punishment
0   I don't feel I am being punished.
1   I have a feeling that something bad may happen to me.
2   I feel I am being punished or will be punished.
3a   I feel I deserve to be punished.
3b   I want to be punished.

G Self-dislike
0   I don't feel disappointed in myself.
1a   I am disappointed in myself.
1b   I don't like myself.
2   I am disgusted with myself.
3   I hate myself.

H Self-accusation
0   I don't feel I am any worse than anybody else.
1   I am critical of myself for my weaknesses or mistakes.
2   I blame myself for my faults.
3   I blame myself for everything bad that happens.

I Suicidal ideas
0   I don't have any thoughts of harming myself.
1   I have thoughts of harming myself but I would not carry them out.
2a   I feel I would be better off dead.
2b   I feel my family would be better off if I were dead.
3a   I have definite plans about committing suicide.
3b   I would kill myself if I could.

J Crying
0   I don't cry any more than usual.
1   I cry more now than I used to.

2   I cry all the time now, I can't stop it.
3   I used to be able to cry but now I can't cry at all even though I want to.

K Irritability
0   I am no more irritated now than I ever am.
1   I get annoyed or irritated more easily than I used to.
2   I feel irritated all the time.
3   I don't get irritated at all at the things that used to irritate me.

L Social withdrawal
0   I have not lost interest in other people.
1   I am less interested in other people now than I used to be.
2   I have lost most of my interest in other people.
3   I have lost all my interest in other people and don't care about them at all.

M Indecisiveness
0   I make decisions about as well as ever.
1   I try to put off making decisions.
2   I have great difficulty in making decisions.
3   I can't make decisions at all anymore.

N Body image change
0   I don't feel I look any worse than I used to.
1   I am worried that I am looking older or unattractive.
2   I feel that there are permanent changes in my appearance and they make me look unattractive.
3   I feel that I am ugly or repulsive looking.

O Work retardation
0   I can work about as well as before.
1a It takes extra effort to get started at doing a task or job.
1b I don't work as well as I used to.
2   I have to push myself very hard to do anything.
3   I can't do any work at all.

P Insomnia

0   I can sleep as well as usual.
1   I wake up more tired in the morning than I used to.
2   I wake up 1–2 hours earlier than usual and find it hard to get back to sleep.
3   I wake up early every day and can't get more than 5 hours sleep.

Q Fatiguableness

0   I don't get any more tired than usual.
1   I get tired more easily than I used to.
2   I get tired from doing anything.
3   I get too tired from doing anything.

R Anorexia

0   My appetite is no worse than usual.
1   My appetite is not as good as it used to be.
2   My appetite is much worse now.
3   I have no appetite at all anymore.

S Weight loss

0   I haven't lost much weight, if any, lately.
1   I have lost more than 5 pounds.
2   I have lost more than 10 pounds.
3   I have lost more than 15 pounds.

T Somatic preoccupation

0   I am no more concerned about my health than usual.
1   I am concerned about aches and pains or upset stomach or constipation.
2   I am so concerned with how I feel or what I feel that it's hard to think of much else.
3   I am completely absorbed in what I feel.

U Loss of libido

0   I have not noticed any recent change in my interest in sex.
1   I am less interested in sex than I used to be.
2   I am much less interested in sex now.
3   I have lost interest in sex completely.

Scoring: 0–9 = normal range; 10–15 = mild depression;

16–19 = mild to moderate depression; 20–29 = moderate to severe depression; 30–63 = severe depression.

(From Beck A.T.: *Depression: Causes and Treatment*, Philadelphia, 1967, University of Pennsylvania Press.)

What might help   The first point to make here is that mild to moderate cases of depression are relatively common, are usually short lived and can clear up by themselves. Unhappiness is not fun, but in many circumstances it is perfectly normal.

However, for some people, depression can become a very serious pervasive condition. If the depression is caught in time, psychotherapy (see Chapter 6), exercise, diet, emotional support and understanding can get a sufferer through. In many cases, the person experiencing the depression will have enough insight and motivation and hopefully support to work towards getting over their depression, although at times it might feel overwhelmingly difficult. In the short term, anti-depressants can be prescribed by a GP, but it cannot be overemphasised that these are only effective for a very short period of time. Anti-depressants can take between two to four weeks to begin to affect the depression; and although they can be helpful in the short term, they only deal with the symptoms of depression and not the causes, which need to be tackled through other means such as therapy or change in life-style or situation.

However, some people find it impossible to deal with their depression without fairly high levels of support, perhaps even needing hospitalisation. And this should be recognized as acceptable, rather than a sign of weakness or madness. Where a patient is hospitalised with depression, the likelihood is that drug treatment will be part of a wider regime that includes counselling (see Chapter 6), occupational therapy (see Chapter 7) and close observation from a skilled nursing team. For people whose depression is very resistant, very deep and life-threatening, electro-convulsive therapy may be an option (see chapter 7).

One of the major alternatives or complementary strategies to drug treatments is to try and change your behaviour, which in turn will affect the way you feel. People who are depressed tend to walk slowly with their head down and shoulders stooped. They tend to sit with their head in their hands. Although it is difficult to maintain for a long period of time, attempting to walk and sit upright with your head held high can make a difference to how you feel.

Research has found that people suffering from depression have lower levels of the neurotransmitters serotonin and noradrenalin in their brains. It is not known whether this is a cause or effect of the depression, but readjusting the levels of these transmitters is an important part of helping someone overcome their depression. Some drug treatments are designed to do this.

Alternative approaches to drugs for depression include the following. These can be used as complementary care as well.

- Consider some psychotherapy or counselling — see Chapter 6 for detailed information.
- Eat a regular diet of wholefoods. Vitamin B6 supplements have also been found to be helpful.
- Exercise — physical activity alters the levels of neurotransmitters in the brain, the more vigorous the exercise the greater the effect. When someone is depressed there is a lowering in the levels of serotonin in the brain. Exercise increases the level of serotonin. If you think about it, it makes good sense. When you exercise vigorously, you become tired but relaxed. Lack of physical activity can also cause a drop in serotonin levels and so when you are depressed and inactive, this can exacerbate your problem.
- Pay attention to the way you look. Your self-image and self-esteem will already be quite low, and if you neglect yourself these will only drop further. Trying to look good can go a long way to making you feel good as well.
- Allow yourself to get involved in non-demanding social activities. You may feel as though you want to avoid

people much of the time, but this withdrawal is counterproductive when trying to combat depression.

- Learn to recognise when you are experiencing a lowering in mood; even when depressed, people often experience mood swings. These are the times when it is essential to keep to a positive programme, or ask for extra help and support from those around you. If you live on your own, then try to spend time in places where other people are but where they will not make too many demands on you, such as parks or libraries.
- Try to give yourself some small reward for every activity you set yourself and achieve. For example, if you go for a one mile walk, even if you hated it, reward yourself with something that you used to enjoy before you experienced your depression, such as a hot milky drink in front of the television.
- Don't be too hard on yourself. If you have a bad day, then try to accept it philosophically. Everyone has bad days. It's just that yours are more frightening and miserable because you are already at a low.
- AT ALL COSTS AVOID ALCOHOL.

It must be remembered that depression is often not easy to shift. If you feel that you cannot deal with your depression by yourself, particularly if it is affecting your life in such an adverse way that the consequences (such as the loss of your job) may be devastating and very detrimental to your life, then don't be afraid to ask for help. Asking for help is a sign of strength not weakness. Your GP may well be helpful. He or she may be a counsellor themselves or may refer you on to a specialist such as a community mental health (psychiatric) nurse or a clinical psychologist.

Drug dependence
The word dependence is more accurate and increasingly more popular than the term addiction. It refers to a physical, psychological or social need for a substance; a state whereby a person is unable or feels themselves unable to function without the help of a substance. The

substance in itself may not be physically addictive, although the person may become reliant psychologically upon it.

People can become dependent on a variety of substances — alcohol, tranquillisers, heroin, and household fluids to name but a few. Alcohol dependence is dealt with separately (see pp. 000–00) and this section looks at addiction to other substances, some of which are expensive and difficult to get hold of and others that can be obtained from supermarket shelves.

Addiction or dependence can be physical and/or psychological. It is not possible to predict which people will eventually become dependent and so ANY potentially addictive substance should be used with great care, if not avoided altogether.

Signs and symptoms   These vary depending on the substance that is being abused, and distinction should be made between the signs and symptoms or recent and long-term use.

• Tranquillisers (benzodiazepines eg Librium, Valium, Ativan)
Tranquillisers, prescribed for anxiety by GP's or hospital doctors, are only effective for a few weeks and long term use can result in addiction. Between 15–35 per cent of long term (six months +) users will experience withdrawal symptoms including anxiety, nightmares, difficulty in sleeping, palpitations, sweating, nausea, loss of appetite.

• Opiates (eg heroin)
Recent use ('fix'): dreamy, far-away manner, eyes glazed but wide open, pin-point pupils, slow, slurred speech, impaired concentration, anorexia, rubbing of face, particularly eyes, chin and nose, scratching of arms and legs, a drowsy wakefulness, frequent use of the toilet, fresh puncture (injection) marks on the body (arms, ankles, groin).

As the effects of the 'fix' wear off (known as 'coming down'), the user will experience a runny nose, sweating, yawning and will feel irritable and restless.

Long-term use may result in a deterioration in appearance as the user loses interest in this, weight loss and disinterest in food, pallor and a change in lifestyle such as staying out all night. Burnt through matches and blackened tinfoil are a sign of opiate use.

• Amphetamines
Recent use: elation, giggling for no apparent purpose, dilated pupils, dry mouth and lips, trembling, very active and talkative, often with a lack of tact.

As the effect of the amphetamines wears off, the user will be low in mood and rather paranoid, lethargic and irritable; eyes will be very sensitive to light.

• Barbiturates
Recent use: behaviour is similar to that induced by alcohol consumption — slurred voice, drunk appearance, staggering, drowsiness and general intoxication. People who have been abusing barbiturates can become aggressive or violent.

• Cannabis
Recent use: euphoria, silliness, giggling, glazed eyes, faraway expressions, slurred speech, periods of excitability, relaxed manner, unsteady gait.

Long-term use: deterioration in memory and concentration, passive attitude, reddened eyes, dry cough.

• Hallucinogens (LSD,'magic' mushrooms)
Recent use: abrupt mood changes, far-away expression, glazed eyes, fascination with everyday objects, out-of-place laughter, extreme reaction to auditory and visual stimuli.

As the effects wear off there is a flatness of mood and emotions. Flashbacks may occur; these are spontaneous episodes that cause the suffer to 'relive' a previous drug-induced state.

• Solvents
Runny nose, spots or rash round the mouth, red watery eyes, hacking cough, unusual or disturbed behaviour, moodiness, headaches, stomach ache and feelings of nausea, smell of solvents or glue on breath.

Possible causes   People usually start using drugs through curiosity combined with availability, the desire to 'experiment' (the exception being prescribed drugs, such as tranquillisers, where availability is combined with perceived need). The general interest is in the ability of a substance to give a feeling of well-being, euphoria or a 'high'. Many people go through this stage and come out the other side experiencing no major difficulties. Some may not like the experience, others may be wary of addiction. However, some people turn to drugs as a way of blotting out emotional pain or unpleasant realities, and the use becomes abuse — an uncontrollable dependency on addictive substances. For these people the drug can become a habit and as the body develops a tolerance to the drug more is needed each time to achieve the same effect. As physical addiction takes a hold, being without the drug can cause very unpleasant feelings (withdrawal effects) that only taking the drug or a prescribed substitute can prevent.

The main types of substances that are abused are:

- Minor tranquilisers, eg Librium and Valium
- Sedatives and narcotics, eg heroin, barbiturates
- Stimulants, eg cocaine, amphetamines
- Hallucinogens, eg LSD
- Solvents, eg glue, hairspray

What might help   There are different philosophies when it comes to dealing with addiction. Some treatment centres will start by detoxifying the person. This might be done by providing nursing care until the person is free from the drugs in his or her system and, where possible, following up with psychotherapy and support through groups, or perhaps by offering a substitute for the addictive substance. Methodone, which is sometimes used to aid withdrawal from heroin, is controversial because while it removes the craving for heroin it is in itself addictive.

Even more controversial is the approach used by a few drug treatment centres in the United Kingdom whereby the philosophy is not one of detoxification and helping people get off and stay off drugs, but one of maintenance by supplying the patient with legally prescribed doses of the drug in question in the belief that this will cut down on the extent and power of the black market in drugs, and avoid overdoses and the risk of the spread of other life-threatening conditions such as AIDS contracted through needle sharing.

Although there may be disagreement on the treatment approach, there is more consensus on the issue of resources for helping substance abusers. These are woefully inadequate and very dependent on voluntary organisations. These include Libra, SCODA, South Wales Association for the Prevention of Addiction, Turning Point and NHS drug dependence clinics. Your local GP, Samaritans or MIND group will be able to direct you to local drug dependence agencies.

For people who have found themselves dependent on tranquillisers, or who have been using tranquillisers for a long period of time (from several months to years) and feel they need help and advice to come off these, TRANX, the National Tranquilliser Advisory Council, can provide advice and counselling.

Huntington's chorea
See Dementia/deterioration of the brain above.

Hyperactivity
Hyperactivity is usually associated with children, although hyperactive behaviour can occur in adults too.

Signs and symptoms   Activity levels over and above those normally associated with age, stage of development and situation, difficulty in concentration and very limited attention span, rapidly changing moods.

Possible causes   There is evidence of a link between diet and hyperactivity in children, with many food additives believed to be at the root of the problem. Physical illness, such as an infection, can also cause hyperactivity. Other theories include imbalances in the chemical messenger systems in the brain and environmental pollutants, such as aluminium and lead.

What might help   Behaviour therapy, modified diet, relaxation.

The Hyperactive Children's Support Group offer advice to parents of hyperactive children.

Hypochondria

A person is said to be suffering from hypochondria when he or she is convinced that they have some form of disease or illness, despite the fact that no evidence can be found to support these beliefs.

Although this type of reaction is linked to other mental health problems, such as anxiety and illness phobias, it is not uncommon for people who have been convinced for some time that they have a particular disease to die of that disease, despite doctors being unable to find any trace of it when the patient first expresses his or her anxieties. Whether this is because the sufferer's mind is aware of the onset of the disease long before it is detectable or the conviction is so powerful that it creates the disease can only be speculated upon.

Hysteria

Hysteria is usually associated with women screaming their heads off and having their faces slapped. However, in psychiatric parlance, hysteria is a physical complaint that has no physical source. For instance, sudden paralysis with no evidence of trauma or stroke. Hysterical blindness was far more common in the earlier part of this century than it is now and was known to be experienced by soldiers during the first and second world wars.

Hysteria can also show itself in the form of amnesia. This is referred to as a dissociative state. In some very rare cases the sufferer may take on another personality.

Signs and symptoms   Physical symptoms, such as paralysis, fits, memory loss or illness, that have no apparent physical cause.

Possible causes   The Freudian explanation for hysterical conditions are that they are the result of repressed anxiety. Some people are described as having an hysterical personality, generally meaning they tend to be attention seeking and experience extreme mood swings.

What might help   Psychotherapy, hypnotherapy, behaviour therapy or family therapy (see Chapter 6).

Mania

This mood disorder is the opposite in nature to depression. Rather than suffering from an absence of energy, extreme unhappiness and despair, people who have a manic episode experience boundless energy, a feeling of euphoria and the belief that they are very successful. Unlike depression where the sufferer usually knows that something is wrong, the person suffering from mania is unlikely to have insight into their condition. If left untreated, mania can cause a person to collapse and even die from exhaustion.

If the person suffering from mania also experiences, at times, depression they are said to be susceptible to manic depression (see below).

Unlike depression which is usually a neurotic disorder, mania and manic depression are psychotic disorders.

Signs and symptoms   Very elated mood, optimistic, excitable and impulsive, masses of energy, often not needing to eat or sleep, can be very disinhibited particularly sexually, speech can be very rapid with rapidly changing thoughts and ideas. These ideas may often be very grand in nature, the person believing they are very rich or powerful. The person suffering from mania will be unaware that anything is wrong with them. On the contrary, they will feel extremely well because they are so 'high'.

Possible causes   Chemical imbalance in the body or brain, extreme stress, reaction to some drug treatments such as antidepressants, unconscious reaction against underlying depression.

What might help   Drug treatment is often necessary in order to slow down and stabilise the person suffering from mania. For extreme cases, major tranquillising drugs, such as chlorpromazine or haloperidol, might be used. In less severe cases it might be possible to stabilise the sufferer's mood with lithium carbonate (see Chapter 9). Prevention particularly in the form of stress management, is essential for people who may experience bouts of mania or a manic-depressive condition, in order to prevent relapses which may be stress-induced even with maintenance on lithium.

Manic depression

Depression has been explained in some detail above, as it is the most common manifestation of mental distress. As was said, depression is something that most people experience to some degree, and for some it can be quite severe. For about 5–15 per cent of those suffering from depression, their depressive experience alternates with one of mania (see above).

Signs and symptoms   Mania and depression are both described above. The evidence that a person may be suffering from manic depression results from swings from mania to depression, or vice-versa, on a cyclical basis. The period between these swings can vary from a few weeks to years.

Possible causes   Like so many other mental health problems, the contributing factors will include personality type, upbringing, stressors and ability to cope with these, as well as a possible genetic predisposition. Triggers can include relationship difficulties, work pressure or drug abuse.

What might help   Treatment depends on whether the sufferer is in the depressive or manic phase of their condition (see Depression and Mania above). It may be that a person has to be maintained on lithium (see Chapter 9). Psychotherapy as part of a programme of prevention may well be possible when the person is stable. A stress management programme, wholefood diet (to prevent constipation, particularly if taking lithium), avoidance of alcohol and cigarettes and a measured amount of exercise will all help to maintain a sufferer's well-being. For more information contact the Manic Depression Fellowship, a self-help organisation for sufferers, their relatives and friends.

Obsessive disorders

The main obsessive disorder, although it is relatively rare, is known as obsessive-compulsive neurosis. This type of mental health problem expresses itself through a persistent desire to carry out repetitive actions (compulsion) in response to thoughts that constantly occupy the conscious mind (obsession). For example, a person may become preoccupied by the thought that he has not locked the doors and windows to his house. This thought may become so persistent that the person feels the need to check all the doors and windows, again and again. Although we all experience these types of thoughts and behaviour at some times, they are usually appropriate to what is going on in our lives, such as checking and rechecking the alarm clock because we are afraid we might oversleep and miss an important engagement. However, when this type of thought/behaviour pattern gets out of hand it constitutes a definite mental health problem as it can totally disrupt a person's ability to live a balanced existence. Checking rituals can take hours. Constant hand washing in response to a wholly exaggerated fear of germs can result in torn, bleeding skin. Although this type of mental health problem may be very difficult to understand, it is certain that it causes a great deal of distress to the sufferer.

Signs and symptoms   The following questionnaire, devised by the Institute of Psychiatry in London, is sometimes used as a method of indicating whether or not someone might be suffering from an obsessive-compulsive form of mental health problem:

1. I avoid using public telephones because of possible contamination. T/F
2. I frequently get nasty thoughts and have difficulty getting rid of them. T/F
3. I am more concerned than most people about honesty. T/F
4. I am often late because I can't seem to get through everything on time. T/F
5. I don't worry unduly about contamination if I touch an animal. T/F
6. I frequently have to check things (eg gas or water taps, doors, etc) several times. T/F
7. I have a very strict conscience. T/F
8. I find that almost every day I am upset by unpleasant thoughts that come into my mind against my will. T/F
9. I do not worry unduly if I accidentally bump into somebody. T/F
10. I usually have serious doubts about the simple everyday things I do. T/F
11. Neither of my parents was very strict during my childhood. T/F
12. I tend to get behind in my work because I repeat things over and over again. T/F
13. I use only an average amount of soap. T/F
14. Some numbers are extremely unlucky. T/F
15. I do not check letters over and over again before posting them. T/F
16. I do not take a long time to dress in the morning. T/F
17. I am not excessively concerned about cleanliness. T/F
18. One of my major problems is that I pay too much attention to detail. T/F

19. I can use well-kept toilets without any hesitation. T/F
20. My major problem is repeated checking. T/F
21. I am unduly concerned about germs and diseases. T/F
22. I do not tend to check things more than once. T/F
23. I do not stick to a very strict routine when doing ordinary things. T/F
24. My hands do not feel dirty after touching money. T/F
25. I do not usually count when doing a routine task. T/F
26. I take rather a long time to complete my washing in the morning. T/F
27. I do not use a great deal of antiseptics. T/F
28. I spend a lot of time every day checking things over and over again. T/F
29. Hanging and folding my clothes at night does not take up a lot of time. T/F
30. Even when I do something very carefully I often feel that it is not quite right. T/F

Possible causes Anxiety is a major feature of obsessive-compulsive disorders, although it is often impossible to get to what is causing the anxiety, let alone understand why the anxiety expresses itself through the performance of rituals rather than, say, agoraphobia. There is a personality type that is referred to as obsessive which is characterised by extreme tidiness and cleanliness. However, there is no proven link between this type of personality and mental health problems of an obsessive-compulsive nature.

What might help Behaviour therapy, psychotherapy, relaxation training, drug treatment or ECT (where underlying depression is suspected), family therapy and in very extreme or intolerable cases, psychosurgery.

Paranoia
You have probably experienced feelings of mild paranoia yourself. For instance, you may have walked into a room and everybody stops talking as you appear and you get the

feeling that they were talking about you. Of course, they may have been. But at the same time they may have been talking about something private that they did not want you to hear or it may simply have been a spontaneous lull in conversation. Whatever the reason you will probably soon forget about it and life will carry on as normal. However, paranoid feelings can sometimes get out of hand, so that any action or innocent comment can be interpreted as a threat or someone 'having a go' at you. Where this is extreme, it can become a mental health problem referred to as a paranoid disorder.

Paranoia can be a feature of a mental problem of a schizophrenic nature.

Signs and symptoms   Suspiciousness, belief that people are plotting against one, feeling persecuted or 'got at'.

Paranoid schizophrenia, or paraphrenia, is more likely to affect elderly people. It often takes the form of the belief that relatives or neighbours are plotting against the individual, perhaps to take away their home. Sufferers may also experience auditory hallucinations.

Possible causes   A paranoid disorder might be triggered by the introduction of a drug into the person's system. This might be an illicit drug, such as cannabis or LSD, but equally might be a prescribed medicine that causes an adverse reaction.

A physical illness or build up of toxins in the body can be a contributory factor as can loneliness and rumination (constantly going over things in one's mind).

What might help   Medication may well be the first and foremost treatment. However, psychotherapy, a change in living conditions and community support may well help to prevent further attacks.

Parkinson's disease
This is less a mental health problem and more a physical health problem caused by a disease of the brain. The

majority of sufferers are over 50, although it can affect some people in their thirties or forties.

Signs and symptoms   Tiredness and muscular ridigity and tremor, particularly in the hands and neck. Slow, clumsy movements.

Possible causes   Not known. Although research shows changes in brain chemistry, it is not known if this is a cause or effect of the disease. There is no evidence to suggest that the disease is hereditary.

What might help   Again drug treatment is used, mainly to tackle symptoms.

Phobias
See information under Agoraphobia.

Sociopathic (psychopathic) disorder
Although sociopaths, more commonly known as psychopaths, are dealt with by the mental health services and are included in the Mental Health Act 1983, their problem is one of personality as opposed to disorder, although they can, of course, also experience mental health problems such as depression.

The reason for the increasing preference for the term sociopath as opposed to psychopath, is the belief that it is external, social, forces that are the main causes of the personality disorder rather than something inherently wrong with person's psyche.

Signs and symptoms   A sociopath can be described as someone who persistently commits offences or who behaves aggressively without any experience of conscience, that is, they have no sense of what is right or wrong, good or bad. Not all people with personality disorders end up in prison hospitals. Much depends on the nature of their offence. However, they will experience and show a total disregard for the feelings or needs of others. It is this lack of feeling, conscience or understanding of right or wrong that can make such a person dangerous.

Possible causes   Not known, but again explanations can take a genetic, physical or social nature, ie people are born bad or people are made bad.

What might help   An extensive programme of therapy, treatment to control aggressive symptoms and skilful rehabilitation. Therapeutic communities (see Chapter 7), where the social milieu and group work are the main methods of therapy, are a progressive approach to this type of problem. An example of a therapeutic community that would welcome people with this type of problem is the Henderson Hospital. However, success rates are low, depending on criteria for 'success'.

Schizophrenia
While most people would find it possible to understand the symptoms of many mental health disorders, because they have themselves experienced the symptoms, if only in a very mild form, it is very hard for most people to understand schizophrenia, despite the fact that it is a word often used (usually incorrectly) by the media.

Although the word schizophrenia does literally mean 'splitting of the mind', the term 'split personality' is a misnomer.

Some health care professionals will talk of schizophrenia or schizophrenics as if it is a clear-cut illness, with regular symptoms, just like chicken pox. However, in reality it is not that simple. Many people who have been on the psychiatric treadmill for a considerable period of time may have been variously diagnosed, depending on the diagnosing psychiatrist at the time. One man of 39 I met recently had been variously diagnosed as schizophrenic, having a paranoid psychosis, and a schizoid personality. A young girl of 22 that I nursed had at different times been diagnosed as brain damaged, psychopathic, schizophrenic and manic depressive. Indeed it was enough to drive her mad!

There are symptoms that are generally recognised as being indicative of a schizophrenic illness, although some of them can also be an indication of another psychotic illness, such as manic depression or acute alcohol poisoning. There are also international differences or transcultural differences when it comes to defining schizophrenia.

If you are black you are seven times more likely to be diagnosed as schizophrenic than a white person. In an article 'Mental Health and the Black Community', Ade Coker cites the fact that in Barnsley Hall, a large psychiatric hospital in Birmingham, 50 per cent of the patient population are black and that the most common diagnosis for black people suffering from acute stress is schizophrenia.

In the United States, people suffering from the same signs and symptoms as a person diagnosed as schizophrenic in England would be diagnosed as manic-depressive.

In the Soviet Union there was (until glasnost at least) an illness called political schizophrenia (not a literal translation). Political dissidents would be 'offered' asylum in mental institutions as their beliefs were often seen as a sign of their illness.

Doctors trying to preserve their own sanity 'fit' people into the category of schizophrenia by developing subcategories, including: simple schizophrenia, hebephrenic schizophrenia, catatonic and paranoid schizophrenia, pseudo-neurotic schizophrenia; genuine, nuclear, process, systematic, schizo-affective, schizo-phreniform, cycloid, oneirophrenia, periodic catatonia, shallow, confabulatory, expansive, fantastic and even, would you believe, incoherent schizophrenia.

And so if you behave in a particularly bizarre way then you have a fairly reasonable chance of being labelled schizophrenic. Once labelled, you might have the greatest difficulty convincing those around you that in fact you are really quite normal. In a research experiment in the early 1970s an American psychologist, D.L. Rosenhan, set up an experiment whereby eight completely sane people gained admission to mental hospitals. They did this by reporting to the admitting officer that they had heard voices saying 'empty', 'hollow' and 'thud'. These words were chosen as they could be interpreted as the hallucinating person feeling that their life was empty and hollow. This would be seen as an existential crisis (a crisis of living) and there had never been a report of an existential psychosis. Once admitted the 'patient' behaved perfectly normally, and stopped simulating symptoms. However, in no instance did the clinical staff realise that the person was not 'mad'. Once in hospital and diagnosed, staff continued to see that person as 'schizophrenic' and to record normal behaviour such as writing notes, as evidence of illness.

Clearly, schizophrenia is the most controversial of all mental distress although the issues arguably apply to mental health problems per se. Although controversial there is no doubt that severe stress and life problems can cause some people to develop psychotic symptoms; other people have strange beliefs that to them are very real, although they are beyond the comprehension of others; drug abuse can create a schizophrenic-type illness, as can certain family environments. Research has shown that it may well be possible to inherit a pre-disposition to schizophrenia but schizophrenia itself cannot be inherited like eye-colour.

Whatever the causes of this type of mental distress, statistics show that an average of 8 people in every 1,000 have a risk of developing a schizophrenic-type disorder at some time in their lives. The most likely time is between the ages of 20 and 39.

Signs and symptoms

Passivity experience   Belief that thoughts are being controlled by others (eg aliens) or that thoughts can be heard by others (thought broadcasting).

Auditory hallucinations   The person hears voices that

may well be talking about him or her, usually in a derogatory manner.

Primary delusions   A person may have a complicated delusional belief, such as that the IRA are out to kill him and that nurses or relatives are members of the IRA.

Emotional blunting   People experiencing this type of mental health problem may be unable to show their emotions or may show emotions that are inappropriate, eg laughing at something very sad.

Withdrawal   The person may retreat into a fantasy world where they feel safe.

Disorder of expression   The person may use strange, made-up words (neologisms) or words and sentences that do not make sense (word 'salad').

Disorder of thought   The person may experience one or more disorders in the way they think. For instance they may believe that certain things have a special meaning for them (ideas of reference) or find it impossible to think in abstract terms (concrete thinking).

Possible causes   There are a range of explanations for schizophrenia. There appears to be some evidence, produced from studying the family line of sufferers, that the likelihood of a schizophrenic experience is passed on genetically. However, it is only the likelihood and *not* the schizophrenia. A rise in dopamine levels (dopamine is a chemical the body produces), sometimes triggered by drug abuse, sometimes occurring spontaneously, is believed to be involved.

Although schizophrenia can be experienced by almost anyone, schizophrenia affects only about 1 per cent of the population. People at risk therefore are hard to pinpoint, and so, it follows, is prevention. Research using twins has shown that schizophrenia can be passed through generations of the same family, so this could act as a warning that members of certain families should take additional care to avoid over-stressful situations. However it would be wrong for people to feel singled out or incapacitated because of a family history of this type of illness, as twin research has shown that the tendency for this type of mental disorder will only be inherited by approximately 50 per cent of those potentially at risk.

A psychiatrist called R.D. Laing believed that schizophrenia in an individual was caused by their family and its way of communicating. Faulty parenting, particularly by the mother, was felt by psycho-analysts to be the cause, although this view is losing favour.

However, the fact is that no one knows for sure what the causes of schizophrenia are, and the causes may differ between sufferers.

What may help It is widely felt that there is little or no alternative to drugs for people who suffer from a schizophrenic type condition. However, this depends on the individual and the care available to them.

For some, it is believed that psychotherapy is effective (see Chapter 4). Certainly some people who have suffered from a schizophrenic-type condition have found this approach useful, although it seems to be difficult to convince psychiatrists of the possible benefits.

Life in an environment that is able to support someone who has had an acute schizophrenic experience and who is vulnerable to relapse because of their home situation may bring benefits. Such a supportive community is the basis for the Philadelphia Association, founded by R.D. Laing (see Useful Addresses below); here is a place for people who need understanding, support and a therapeutic environment where medication is not the norm.

However, with the current state of knowledge about this disorder it seems that the greatest opportunity, apart from medications, has to lie in the prevention of relapse. Self-care, as outlined above for people suffering from depression and described in more detail in Chapter 3, may help a vulnerable person avoid relapse, as may understanding, support and relatively stress free social conditions.

USEFUL ADDRESSES

ACCEPT, 200 Seagrave Road, London, SW6 1RQ: 071 381 3155.

Alcohol Concern, 305 Gray's Inn Road, London, WC1X 8QF: 071 833 3471.

Alcohol Counselling Service, 34 Electric Lane, London, SW9 8JT: 071 737 3579.

AA (Alcoholics Anonymous), PO Box 1, Stonebow House, Stonebow, York, YO1 2NJ. 0904 644026.

Alzheimer's Disease Society, 3rd Floor, Bank Buildings, Fulham Broadway, London, SW6 1EP: 071 381 3177

Anorexia Anonymous, 24 Westmoreland Road, London, SW13 9RY: 081 748 3994.

Anorexic Aid, The Priory Centre, 11 Priory Road, High Wycombe, Bucks HP13 6SI.

Anorexic Family Aid, National Information Centre, Sackville Place, 44 Magdalen Street, Norwich, Norfolk, NR3 1JE: 0603 621414.

Association of Self-Help and Community Groups, 7 Chesham Terrace, London, W13 9HX: 071 579 5589.

Association to Combat Huntington's Chorea, (National Administrative Office), Borough House, 34a Station Road, Hinckley, Leics. LE10 1AP: 0455 615558

Association to Combat Huntington's Chorea, (Family Counselling Service), 108 Battersea High Street, London, SW11 3HP: 071 223 7000.

British Epilepsy Association, Crowthorne House, Bigshotte, New Wokingham Road, Wokingham, Berkshire, RG11 3AY: 0344 773122.

Depressives Anonymous (Fellowship of), 36 Chestnut Avenue, Beverley, North Humberside, HU17 9QU: 0482 860619.

Depressives Associated, PO Box 5, Castletown, Portland, Dorset, D15 1BQ.

Drugline, 28 Ballina Street, London, SE23 1DR: 081 291 2341

Epilepsy Association of Scotland, 48 Govan Road, Glasgow, G51 1JL: 041 427 4911.

Ex-Services Mental Welfare Society, Broadway House, The Broadway, London, SW19 1RL: 081 543 6333.

Families Anonymous, 310 Finchley Road, London, NW3 7AG: 071 731 8060.

Gamblers Anonymous, 17/23 Blantyre Street, Cheyne Walk, London, SW10 0DT: 081 551 9096.

Greater London Alcohol Advisory Service, 91–93 Charterhouse Street, London, EC1M 6BT: 071 248 8406.

Hyperactive Children's Support Group, 59 Meadowside, Angmering, Littlehampton, West Sussex, BN16 4BW: 0903 725182 (10 am–3 pm most weekdays).

Manic Depression Fellowship, 13 Roslyn Road, Twickenham, Middlesex, TW1 2AR: 081 892 2811.

National Autistic Society, 276 Willesden Lane, London, NW2 5RB: 081 451 3844

National Schizophrenia Fellowship (England), 78 Victoria Road, Surbiton, KT6 4NS: 081 390 3651.

National Schizophrenia Fellowship (Northern Ireland), Room 6, Bryson House, Bedford Street, Belfast, BT2 7FE: 0232 248006.

National Schizophrenia Fellowship (Scotland), 40 Shandwick Place, Edinburgh, EH2 4RT, 031 226 2025.

National Society for Epilepsy, Chalfont Centre for Epilepsy, Chalfont St Peter, Gerrards Cross, Buckinghamshire, SL9 0RJ: 024 07 3991.

Northern Schizophrenia Fellowship, 38 Collingwood Buildings, Collingwood Street, Newcastle upon Tyne, Tyne and Wear, NE1 1JH: 0632 614343.

National Society for Epilepsy, Chalfont Centre for Epilepsy, Chalfont St Peter, Gerrards Cross, Buckinghamshire, SL9 0RJ: 024 07 3991.

Northern Schizophrenia Fellowship, 38 Collingwood Buildings, Collingwood Street, Newcastle upon Tyne, Tyne and Wear, NE1 1JH: 0632 614343.

Parkinson's Disease Society, 36 Portland Place, London, W1N 3DG: 071 323 1174.

Phobics Society, 4 Cheltenham Road, Chorlton cum Hardy, Manchester, M21 1QN: 061 881 1937.

2
YOU KNOW WHAT YOUR PROBLEM IS, DON'T YOU!

Amateur psychologists are as common as cat's fleas. And usually just about as welcome. They lurk everywhere. Often disguised as friends or relatives they lie in wait until you are feeling either extremely happy or extremely miserable, at which point they loom up in front of you, eyes misty with sympathy, head nodding from sheer weight of their burgeoning wisdom and then bestow upon you, lucky soul, the full benefit of their insight. Of course, they say, you know what your problem is! They then proceed to tell you, in your own interests, of course, where you don't quite measure up to, well, whatever it is we are all supposed to measure up to. No-one's perfect of course, they continue, but really, couldn't you try just a little harder?

You, of course, probably did know what your problem was, but had done a passably good job of denying the fact that really, somewhere deep down inside, you harbour rage, jealousy, envy and homicidal thoughts about your mother.

Thanks to your benefactor's insight, denial, your number one coping strategy, has taken a mortal blow. If you were feeling happy, sure as eggs are eggs, you don't now. If you were feeling as miserable as sin and life was looking pretty hopeless in any case, then you might well make your way to the top of a very tall building or to the bottom of a very deep river.

In most areas of our lives there is always someone or something around to remind us of our shortcomings. Advertising, competition, sexual stereotyping, social norms. Psychologists work day and night to establish what is normal and abnormal, average and below-average, typical and atypical. And manufacturers, the media, the medical profession, educationalists and a whole score more respond not to uniqueness, individuality or eccentricity, but to that bit of us that can comfortably be counted and categorised. Ideals are held up against which we are measured or against which we should measure ourselves.

The problem with ideals is that they are usually unattainable for all but a few. There can usually only be one winner of a competition or best pupil in a class. Ideals are often artificially created, like advertising images. They are held up as something we should aspire to. It's not what we are, but what would we be if only ...!

The one changing ideal that makes me grin through gritted teeth (forgive the badly mixed metaphor) is the cultural swing in bosoms. In true tabloid tradition the 'fashion' headlines pronounce 'Big boobs are in', followed the next year by 'Big boobs are out'. Radical surgery and breast binding aside, it is virtually impossible to successfully manipulate the size, shape or proportion of one's chest in order to maintain social approval. However, for centuries women have tried to do this and corsetry manufacturers have no doubt become very rich on the proceeds.

So much emphasis is placed on how we look rather than what we are that an enormous amount of our very precious time and energy is wasted on pleasing others and losing our selves in the process. By chasing some elusive illusion of perfection we competently entrench ourselves in no-win situations.

No-win situations by no means just affect women. A man might risk his life in order to conform and yet be rejected when he does because of a change in events outside his control. Soldiers who fought in the Vietnam war found themselves in a no-win situation of horrendous proportions. There were those who seriously doubted the morality of the war (if any war can be called moral), but were nonetheless conscripted. Faced with a conflict between their beliefs and the public view of the conflict they were required to enter, they may have considered refusing to fight (registering as conscientious objectors); many did and were called cowards and traitors, and were punished. Others fought because they believed it was the right thing to do. But the war was seen as unacceptable by many nations and it was a war America lost. American society's shame over Vietnam caused a wholesale rejection of the men who had fought there. The result was that many Vietnam veterans suffered severe psychological hardship both during and after the conflict. And there have been many suicides.

Of course, some people are better at dealing with life crises than others, and it is often how we learn to cope with life's little knocks during our early years that has such an important bearing on how we cope with what becomes life's body blows during the rest of our lives.

Sadly, for some, life starts dealing out body blows at a very early stage, before they have had a chance to practise with the little knocks, with life's warm-up rounds. It is hard to imagine what it must be like for a child not yet of school age who has to come to terms with loss, rejection, physical, psychological or sexual abuse unless we have actually had the experience and had to deal with the emotional consequences — the pain, the anger, the guilt, the fear.

Even for those who have not had to deal with such major trauma, enormous long-term damage to mental well-being can be inflicted by relentless criticism and lack of expressed affection.

Our early childhood experiences lay the foundation for how we see the world and our perception of how the world sees and treats us. It also profoundly influences the skills we develop in order to deal with future experiences.

By the time we reach adulthood we may well have sustained more than our fair share of emotional damage and need some help in putting this right. In short we might need to do some work on our own mental health.

MENTAL HEALTH

Is there an ultimate in mental health that we ought to be chasing? You would certainly think so to listen to some humanistic psychologists. The belief that we can continue to develop to some infinite degree gives the potential for a full-time career in self-analysis, self-development, self-fascination and, well, more self-fascination. In fact Narcissus would be hard pushed to compete.

For A.H. Maslow, an American psychologist, self-actualisation is the ultimate state of being.

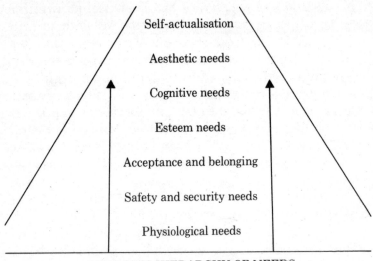

MASLOW'S HIERARCHY OF NEEDS

This theory maintains that we attend to our most essential needs as and when they arise, and that these needs can be arranged in a hierarchy. For instance, our most basic bodily needs are for food, fluids and air to breathe.

Once these basic physiological needs have been satisfied, then we attend to our need for safety and security, for instance renting or buying a home away from a district with a high crime rate. Once we feel warm and safe, fed and watered, then we look to our need to be accepted by others, to feel good about ourselves, to feed our intellect and surround ourselves with things of beauty and finally to self-actualise. That is, to reach a point of spiritual oneness with the world, to realise our true self.

Other thoughts on what might be described as extreme mental health come from Dr Robin Skynner, who had the good fortune to be the therapist to help John Cleese to sort himself out. His criteria for supreme mental health include the ability to recover one's emotional equilibrium within a fairly short period following the death of a wife or husband and to move forward with a new, successful relationship.

Another description of a mentally healthy person is one who can solve problems in a mature way, someone who can deal with crises within the supportive framework of family and social networks (Crawford A.L. and Kilander V.C. 1985, *Psychiatric and Mental Health Nursing* 6th edn, F.A. Davis, Philadelphia, Pennsylvania). My belief is that you *cannot* measure exceptional mental health. It is not something that can be compared, like the length of a penis or examination results.

In order to get by as well as we can there are certain stumbling blocks we need to avoid or negotiate successfully in our everyday lives. And the major one of these is stress.

UNDERSTANDING STRESS

As we grow up, we have to cope with increasing levels of responsibility. We become aware of the expectations others have of us, and we develop our own expectations. We find ourselves in a world where we have to 'succeed', and where success and achievement have been defined by others. Our parents, peers, employers, patrons — all these and more make it very difficult for us to define for ourselves what we want out of life.

Life, and consequently our mental health, becomes a matter of getting to know and understand ourselves and what we want, achieving what we can and coming to terms with what we can't.

There are different demands on us at different times in our lives, some inevitable, some self-inflicted. Moving house is usually a self-inflicted stress, whereas being made redundant is a stress imposed by someone else. How we cope with these demands is to a large extent how we grow as people. When faced with a demand we check out resources. Can we cope? If yes, we move ahead fairly confident of a positive outcome. If we perceive our resources as being inadequate, we may ask for help or develop our resources in some way. However, it is when we feel our resources are inadequate and we are unable to gain further resources that we can start to feel overwhelmed, or in popular terms, stressed.

Stress is a very individual thing. What one person may find unbearably stressful another might thrive on. For instance, I feel quite ill just watching brokers working in a City stock exchange market, waving their arms about with a telephone glued to their ear. To think that some of those people have travelled for over two hours on an overcrowded commuter train makes me want to question their sanity. But following the stock market crash, it was the loss of jobs, excitement and status that appeared to be the stressor for the unemployed yuppie stockbroker.

The level of stress felt appears to depend on the individual's perception of the stressor as well as their perception of their ability to deal with the situation. Hans Selye, one of the pioneers of stress research, identified four levels of stress:

- **Understress**: Too little stress takes away the sense of challenge in our life and with this our feelings of achievement. We are unmotivated and lose our sense of purpose in life.
- **Eustress**: At this stage we are getting just the right amount of stress in our lives — not too little, not too much. Our life is fairly well balanced and we feel in control.
- **Overstress**: When we are overstressed we experience a very uncomfortable level of stress. There is never enough time to get everything done. We cannot relax or take time off from work without feeling guilty. Yet, we

find that no matter how hard we work, we never seem to achieve what we set out to .

- **Distress**: Once this stage is reached we are very much out of control. We become ill, either physically or mentally. We may turn to short-term stimulants, such as alcohol, sleeping pills or tranquillisers. If unalleviated, this level of distress can kill us.

STRESS AND YOU

Trying to understand ourselves and learning to recognise what it is that makes us feel stressed is an essential part of a mental health self-care regime for everybody.

However, before you can cope with stress in a positive and effective manner, you need to become skilled at recognising your own responses to stress.

Recognising the early signs of stress is not as easy as it sounds. Too often we do not appreciate that we are over-stressed until we actually succumb to a physical or mental health problem.

Despite the fact that we can accept, at an intellectual level, that an event, such as a bereavement, moving house, a broken relationship or a burglary, is stressful, we feel somehow we should be able to 'cope'. Sadly, coping seems to a lot of people to mean managing by themselves, not having to ask for help. Asking for help, support or assistance is still perceived as weakness. Talking about the problems you are experiencing is viewed as 'burdening others'.

Damaging stress tends to be insidious. It builds up without our noticing it, over a period of time. The human mind and body has a tremendous capacity for adaptation, so we often feel that we are in charge or in control of our responses for quite some time after the damage has begun. It is a little bit like drinking alcohol; by the time we get to the stage where we recognise we have had enough, it is often too late. The effects overwhelm us. Stress, like alcohol, also distorts our perception.

We then start to notice symptoms like fatigue, waking

up feeling tired, lacking motivation to do even fairly simple tasks. If left too long we can get to a stage where we can hardly function and may collapse, physically or mentally. It is important to realise then that understanding how we respond to various stresses, our strengths and our weaknesses in certain situations, and how we feel as we become stressed, is a vital part of prevention of mental health problems and the promotion of general well-being.

Possible signs of stress

- Marked loss of concentration
- Feeling of tiredness, even on waking
- Early morning waking/difficulty getting to sleep/ nightmares
- Increased use of alcohol or cigarettes
- Increased irritability
- Loss of perspective
- Tendency to withdraw from social activities
- Increased sensitivity to criticism
- Change in eating patterns
- Tension
- Rebelliousness
- Stomach pains, in knots
- Shaky hands
- Nervous twitch, for instance in eyelid
- Loss of self-confidence
- Memory lapses
- Uncomfortable feelings of pressure
- Palpitations
- Stiff jaw
- Nail biting
- Nausea
- Diarrhoea
- Panic attacks
- Feelings of anger, aggression and hostility
- Tearfulness
- Neglected appearance
- Physical agitation, eg tapping fingers, restless legs
- Dry mouth

- Sweaty hands, cold fingers
- Grey complexion
- Haggard looks
- Strong feelings of guilt

CAUSES OF STRESS

Stress is the result of pressure being applied to one thing by another. Depending on the amount of pressure applied and the object's ability to resist or bend with the pressure, the object will not snap or break. Take, for instance, a strand of uncooked spaghetti. If you take it gently between the fingers of each hand and bend it gently, it will take quite a bit of pressure (bending) before it snaps.

Our wrists and ankles are designed to take quite a bit of pressure and bend quite flexibly. However, too much pressure too quickly can result in pain or even a fracture.

The same applies to our minds.

Psychologically we are usually very good at adapting to the level of pressure around us. However, when that pressure gets too great we start to feel psychological pain. And if the pressure is kept up or is forced on us before we are ready to deal with it, our psychological structure can also snap.

Research has shown that psychological pressures come in the form of life events.

Measuring Stress Levels

Event	Stress Points
Death of spouse/partner	100
Divorce	73
Marital separation/break up of live-in relationship	65
Jail term	63
Death of a close family member	63
Personal injury or illness	53
Marriage	50
Loss of job	47
Marital reconciliation	45

Retirement	45
Change in family member's health	44
Pregnancy	40
Sex difficulties	39
Addition to family	39
Business readjustment	39
Change in financial state	38
Death of a close friend	37
Change to different line of work	36
Change in number of arguments with spouse	35
Taking out a large mortgage or loan	31
Foreclosure on mortgage or loan	30
Change in work responsibilities	29
Son or daughter leaving home	29
Trouble with in-laws	29
Outstanding personal achievement	28
Spouse/partner begins or stops work	26
Starting or finishing school	26
Change in living conditions	25
Revision of personal habits	24
Trouble with boss	23
Change in work hours or conditions	20
Change in residence	20
Change in school	20
Change in recreational habits	19
Change in church activities	19
Change in social activities	18
Taking out a small mortgage or loan	17
Change in sleeping habits	16
Change in number of family gatherings	15
Change in eating habits	15
Holiday	13
Christmas season	12
Minor violation of the law	11

Scoring:
Less than 150, 30 per cent probability of developing an illness (ie average risk at most).
150–299, 50 per cent probability of developing an illness.
Over 300, 80 per cent probability of developing an illness.

(From Holmes and Rahe, *Schedule of Recent Life Events.*)

These are stressful events that happen to most people. By themselves they can cause varying degrees of emotional pain and discomfort, but are usually manageable. What causes difficulties for us is:

- Experiencing several of these together.
- Experiencing a major stressful event in an already stressful context, eg someone who is a single parent may be coping with being without a supportive partner and living on a low income, but finds it difficult to cope when there is the additional stress of her mother becoming ill or the death of a close friend. The old saying 'the straw that broke the donkey's back' is a useful one to bear in mind.

Who is most at risk from stress?
Researchers have discovered two types of personality that are most at risk from health problems related to how they respond to stress.

First there is the type 'A' personality. These are the people who may well be heard saying that they thrive on stress. And this may well be true in the short term. This is because their bodies will be producing high levels of the chemical noradrenaline which, like certain types of drugs, is the cause of 'good' feelings such as confidence and elation. Many doctors believe that type 'A' personalities are addicted to the feelings produced by stress. And like any addiction it can have a serious outcome.

Another type of person who is at risk from stress-related illnesses are so-called overachievers. These people are not as aggressively overactive as the type 'A' personality, but they do have very high standards of themselves. They are great 'copers'. They never give in to illness, find it hard to admit to any vulnerability or to admit to their own needs. Indeed this type of person is more likely to put the needs of others first. They are perfectionists and often very self-critical. Many carers have this type of profile.

Although neither of these two personality types may sum you up exactly, you should to be aware of the extent to which you may fall into one category or the other in different situations, and to recognise the danger signs of overstress at the earliest possible stage.

How stressful is your lifestyle?
Completing the following questionnaire might give you some idea.

Tick the box under the number that indicates most accurately where you feel you fit on the scales below and then add up your score.

1 2 3 4 5 6 7

1. Doesn't mind leaving things temporarily   [ ] [ ] [ ] [ ] [ ] [ ] [ ]   Must get things finished once started.

2. Calm and unhurried about appointments   [ ] [ ] [ ] [ ] [ ] [ ] [ ]   Never late for appointments.

3. Not competitive   [ ] [ ] [ ] [ ] [ ] [ ] [ ]   Highly competitive.

4. Listens well, lets others finish speaking.   [ ] [ ] [ ] [ ] [ ] [ ] [ ]   Anticipates others in conversation.

5. Never in a hurry, when pressured.   [ ] [ ] [ ] [ ] [ ] [ ] [ ]   Always in a hurry.

6. Able to wait calmly.   [ ] [ ] [ ] [ ] [ ] [ ] [ ]   Uneasy when waiting.

7. Easy-going.   [ ] [ ] [ ] [ ] [ ] [ ] [ ]   Always full speed ahead.

8. Takes one thing at a time.   [ ] [ ] [ ] [ ] [ ] [ ] [ ]   Tries to do more than one thing at a time, thinks about what to do next.

9. Slow and deliberate in speech.   [ ] [ ] [ ] [ ] [ ] [ ] [ ]   Vigorous and forceful in speech (uses a lot of gestures).

10. Concerned with satisfying his or herself not others.   [ ] [ ] [ ] [ ] [ ] [ ] [ ]   Wants recognition by others for a job well done.

1 2 3 4 5 6 7

11. Slow doing things. [ ] [ ] [ ] [ ] [ ] [ ] [ ] Fast doing things (eating, walking).

12. Easy going. [ ] [ ] [ ] [ ] [ ] [ ] [ ] Hard-driving.

13. Expresses feelings openly. [ ] [ ] [ ] [ ] [ ] [ ] [ ] Holds feelings in.

14. Has a large number of interests. [ ] [ ] [ ] [ ] [ ] [ ] [ ] Has few interests outside work.

15. Satisfied with job. [ ] [ ] [ ] [ ] [ ] [ ] [ ] Ambitious, wants quick advancement on job.

16. Never sets own deadline. [ ] [ ] [ ] [ ] [ ] [ ] [ ] Often sets own deadline.

17. Feels limited responsibility. [ ] [ ] [ ] [ ] [ ] [ ] [ ] Always feels responsible.

18. Never judges things in terms of numbers [ ] [ ] [ ] [ ] [ ] [ ] [ ] Often judges performance in terms of numbers (how much, how many).

19. Casual about work. [ ] [ ] [ ] [ ] [ ] [ ] [ ] Takes work very seriously (works weekends, brings work home).

20. Not very precise. [ ] [ ] [ ] [ ] [ ] [ ] [ ] Very precise (careful about details).

TOTAL SCORE: _____

20–30	B2, relaxed and easy-going
30–59	Moderate type B, coping well
60–79	Neither type A or type B but a healthy AB
80–108	Moderate type A or A2 who should be cautious
109–140	Extreme type A or A1

The Glazer Stress Control Questionnaire

DEALING WITH STRESS

We all develop ways of dealing with stress. Many of them we use consciously, partly perhaps because we do not recognise that we are 'under stress'. Alcohol is one way in which we 'unwind'. Shouting at family members or kicking the cat is another way. However, methods such as these can have adverse effects for us, those around us and, of course, the cat.

What we need to cultivate is a range of positive, healthy methods of dealing with stress — methods that promote our mental well-being rather than threaten it further. Some positive ways of dealing with stress include:

- Walk away from what is causing you the stress (if only to come back and deal with it when you feel stronger).
- Take your mind off the stressor (by absorbing yourself in a hobby, film, book, etc).
- Develop skills to help you deal with the stressor (assertiveness training, simple car maintenance, relaxation techniques or meditation).
- Deep breathing.
- Have a bath.
- Give yourself a treat.
- Sleep.
- Think of times when you have dealt with stress effectively before.
- Find someone to talk to.
- Share your time with people who are rewarding, not those who are critical and judgemental.
- Join a support group if appropriate.

Looking at the way you breathe

How we breathe is important to our understanding of, and coping with, tension, anxiety and stress.

How we breathe affects the levels of oxygen and carbon dioxide in our blood, which in turn affects how well we do or do not feel.

Although it was once believed that taking deep breaths in front of an open window was the clue to well-being, it is now known that it is detrimental to take in too much oxygen. Hyperventilation or overbreathing washes too much carbon dioxide out of the blood, which results in unpleasant side-effects. Hyperventilation can be experi-

enced by unfit people who engage
squash or running and who are const
resulting in dizziness and fainting.

Fast breathing mainly from the uppe
matic of anxiety. Slow breathing, using t
the lungs with particular emphasis on
contributes to a lowering in feelings of anxie   ..ies of
emergency, feelings of anxiety can be lowered .y breathing
into a paper bag for several minutes or until symptoms
subside. This cuts down on the amount of oxygen in the
body by breathing in exhaled carbon dioxide.

To know if you are breathing correctly, lie on your back,
place one hand on the upper part of your chest and the
other on top of your tummy. Breathe out first and then
breathe in. If you are doing this comfortably, your tummy
will rise at the beginning of the breath. If your chest moves
first your breathing is inefficient. After breathing out, wait
a moment before breathing in as much air as the body
wants. A few breaths like this before starting relaxation
will be beneficial. Controlled breathing can be very helpful
whenever you are in a stressful situation, such as a job interview or meeting difficult people.

If anxiety and tension make you want to cry in difficult
situations, when it would be better for you to control this
(crying releases tension), take a deep breath and hold it
while pushing the sob down to where you can control it.

Relaxation exercises

Before doing relaxation exercises, it helps to do some gentle
stretching exercises. This is because much of the pain and
discomfort we experience, such as headaches, neck and
shoulder pains, cramps, pains in joints and so on, are
created through muscle tension that is stimulated by the
mind.

If our mind tells our body that we need to be alert
because there is some threat (a deadline not being met, an
aggressive boss picking up a mistake we have made, insuf-
ficient money to meet our basic needs), the body responds
by getting itself into the 'fight or flight' mode. That is, we

to threats by fighting the source or running away. was particularly important in the days when we were hunters and when the fight or flight mechanism triggered an actual physical response. However, today many threats are psychological and it is much harder to run away from what is in our minds (hence many people's recourse to alcohol and drugs). Added to this is a general lack of physical exercise, which means that the products of muscle tension are not burnt up by the body. These waste products build up and cause feelings of being unwell. Muscle relaxation aids the disposal of these waste products.

Deep muscle relaxation

There are several methods of relaxation. The one that has perhaps been most favoured is deep muscle relaxation, because psychologists have discovered that deep muscle relaxation and anxiety cannot exist simultaneously. Therefore you can gain a great deal of control over anxiety, which accompanies many mental health problems, as well as being a problem in its own right.

Everyday stress creates a build up of stimulation in a certain part of the brain known as the hypothalamus. This creates a sensitivity to further stress and eventually a form of overload. Deep muscle relaxation is a way of cutting down on the stimulation to the hypothalamus and thereby preventing over-sensitivity. Once skilled at deep muscle relaxation you will achieve a greater sense of mental and physical balance and an enhanced sense of well-being. Deep muscle relaxation is a skill that has to be learnt, and like any new skill this takes time and practice.

There are many different methods of relaxation. My favourite is guided fantasy which allows the mind to roam, away from the problems that preoccupy it, and into a world where serenity and self-awareness can be found.

Most mental health centres (contact your local health authority for the address) run relaxation groups, as do mental health day hospitals, some GP clinics, evening class groups and so on.

Preparation:
Sit in a comfortable chair, or better still, lie down. Choose a quiet, warm room, when you are not too tired and where you will not be interrupted.

If you are sitting, take off your shoes, uncross your legs, and rest your arms along the arms of the chair.

If you are lying down, lie on your back, with your arms at your sides.

Close your eyes, and be aware of your body: notice how you are breathing, and where the tensions in your body are. Make sure you are comfortable.

Breathing:
Start to breathe slowly and deeply, expanding your abdomen as you breathe IN, then raising your rib cage to let more air in, till your lungs are filled right to the top. Hold your breath for a couple of seconds and then breathe OUT slowly, allowing your rib cage and stomach to relax, and empty your lungs completely.

Do not force your breathing. After a time, breathing this way will feel natural.

Keep this slow, deep rhythmic breathing going throughout your relaxation session.

Relaxation:
Now curl your toes and press your feet down. Tense up on an IN breath, hold your breath for 10 seconds while you keep your muscles tense, then relax your muscles and breathe OUT at the same time.

Now press your heels down and bend your feet up. Tense up on a IN breath, hold your breath for 10 seconds; relax your muscles on an OUT breath.

Now tense your calf muscles. Tense up on an IN breath, hold for 10 seconds; relax your muscles on an OUT breath.

Now tense your thigh muscles, straightening your knees

and making your legs stiff. Tense up on an IN breath; hold for 10 seconds; relax your muscles on an OUT breath.

Now make your buttocks tight. Tense up on an IN breath; hold for 10 seconds; relax your muscles on an OUT breath.

Now tense your stomach as if to receive a punch. Tense up on an IN breath; hold for 10 seconds; relax your muscles on an OUT breath.

Now bend your elbows and tense the muscles of your arms. Tense up on an IN breath; hold for 10 seconds; relax your muscles on an OUT breath.

Now hunch your shoulders and press your head back. Tense up on an IN breath; hold for 10 seconds; relax your muscles on an OUT breath.

Now clench your jaws, frown, and screw up your eyes really tight. Tense up on an IN breath; hold for 10 seconds; relax your muscles on an OUT breath.

Now tense all your muscles together. Tense up on an IN breath; hold for 10 seconds; relax all your muscles on an OUT breath.

Stay in this position for a few minutes. If you start to become tense again, repeat the process or work just on the tense area. When you feel ready to get up turn on your side if you are laying down or sit forward gently. Stay there for a few moments before attempting to rise.

Self-hypnosis
Self-hypnosis is a skill that can be learnt, although courses can be quite expensive. Courses are advertised in the MIND and *Human Potential* magazines (addresses at the end of this chapter).

Massage
The touch of another human being is for most people very therapeutic. Most of us do not get enough strokes, either physical or psychological, although we need and want them.

Think of the pleasure you get from touch, be it holding a baby, stroking a cat or cuddling someone close. If we are tired or feeling sad we often stroke ourselves unconsciously. We rub our eyes, run our hands through our hair, stroke our arms, hold our own hands. Touch can help us to relax and the mind knows this.

Massage is a very pleasurable form of relaxation. It is a skill you can learn so as to give yourself a massage in times of stress or to help someone else who is in need of some relaxation and therapeutic touch. Massaging someone else is also therapeutic because of the sense of giving, the concentration and the reciprocal sense of touch.

Courses are available that are not exorbitantly expensive and there are also self-instruction tapes and books. A good example is *Stress and Relaxation: Self-help Techniques for Everyone* by Jane Madders (published by Macdonald Optima).

Meditation

Meditation is a way of clearing the mind of all the clutter and noise it collects. It works on the basis that a relaxed mind induces a relaxed body.

The most common form of meditation is through the use of mantras, words or sayings that concentrate the mind. In his book *How To Meditate* (published by Crucible), the American psychologist, Lawrence LeShan states that there are four main pathways to meditation:

- Through the intellect — the belief being that knowledge and wisdom can be developed to a higher plane through meditation.
- Through the emotions — as in prayer.
- Through the body — by the use of exercises.
- Through action — Aikido, for example, is a form of meditation developed from the martial arts.

Visualisation therapy and intensive meditation are forms of meditation used to tackle certain diseases. Using visualisation therapy the disease, such as cancer, is visualised as perhaps an alien that has entered the body or an invading army. The patient then visualises the white blood cells as the defending force that aims to conquer the invader.

Intensive meditation is a form of deep hypnosis that taps into our inherent but now largely dormant instinct which allows a person to diagnose their own health problem.

Yoga

Although some forms of yoga are deeply spiritual and take a religious dedication to master, there are other forms that are not so demanding. The main aim of yoga is to create a healthy mind in a healthy body. It has been proven scientifically that by using a combination of postures and controlled breathing, yoga reduces tension.

Yoga is best learnt with a qualified teacher although it is possible to obtain books explaining postures and breathing techniques from libraries and bookshops. Many adult education centres offer classes at reasonable prices with discounts for people who are unemployed.

Exercise

Most forms of exercise are a great release for tension. See Chapter 3.

DEALING WITH TENSION

Stress causes tension; tension causes stress. The following are 11 recommendations from the Canadian Mental Health Association for dealing with stress and tension.

1. Talk it out:
If something is worrying you, let it out. Talk over your worries and concerns with someone you trust — partner, parent, family doctor, clergyman, teacher or close friend. Talking relieves the strain and helps you bring problems into perspective.

2. Run away for a while:
Don't spend all your time worrying about your problems. Escape for a while into a book, a movie, a game. True, 'escapism' can be over done, but occasional breaks will help you see things more clearly.

3. Work off your anger:
Give your emotions a rest by switching to physical activities. Dig up the garden. Clean out the garage. Start a building project or hobby.

4. Give in occasionally:
If you find yourself getting into frequent quarrels, stand your ground only when you're sure you're right. Make allowances sometimes for the fact that the other person might be right. It's easier on your system to give in now and then.

5. Give something of yourself:
Doing things for others can take your mind off your own problems. And you'll have a feeling of satisfaction and accomplishment.

6. Tackle one thing at a time:
If your work load seems unbearable, do the most urgent jobs one at a time. Put all the others aside for the time being.

7. Don't try to be perfect:
There are things you like to do best, and things that give you the most satisfaction. Give yourself a pat on the back for those you do well, but don't try to get into the *Guinness Book of Records* with everything you do.

8. Ease up on your criticism:
Don't expect too much of others. Try to remember that each person has his own strengths, his own shortcomings.

9. Don't be too competitive:
Often co-operation is the best approach. When you give other people a break, you often make things easier for yourself, too. If they no longer feel threatened by you, they stop being a threat to you.

10. Make the first move:
Sometimes we have the feeling that we are being left out, slighted or rejected by others. This could be just our imagination. If you make the first move, very often others will respond.

11. Have some fun:
Too much work can be harmful. Old fashioned play is essential for good physical and mental health. Everyone should have a sport, hobby or outside interest that provides a complete break from the work routine.

(From *Psychiatric Nursing*, May–June 1980)

Although all these approaches take time, knowledge and skill to master, it might be helpful to remember that stress management is a vital method of promoting mental well being and avoiding mental health problems. Social reform is the other. Managing our stress level is one vital component of our mental health. Self esteem is another.

MEASURING YOUR SELF-ESTEEM

Right now, this minute, just how good do you feel about yourself? Have a go at the Self-Attitude Questionnaire opposite. (From the *Living Skills* pack, adapted from Rosenberg, M. 1965, *Society and the Adolescent Self-Image*. Princeton NJ, Princeton University Press.)

For each item you will find a statement about yourself, followed by four possible answers: strongly agree, agree, disagree or strongly disagree. Put a ring round the number by whichever answer you choose. Answer truthfully, as you feel now, at this moment.

1. I feel that I'm a person of worth, at least on an equal plane with others.
1 Strongly agree
2 Agree
3 Disagree
4 Strongly disagree

2. I feel as valuable as others.
1 Strongly agree
2 Agree
3 Disagree
4 Strongly disagree

3. All in all I am inclined to feel that I am a failure.
1 Strongly agree
2 Agree
3 Disagree
4 Strongly disagree

4. As a person I am quite acceptable.
1 Strongly agree
2 Agree
3 Disagree
4 Strongly disagree

5. I don't think very much of myself.
1 Strongly agree
2 Agree
3 Disagree
4 Strongly disagree

6. I take a positive attitude towards myself.
1 Strongly agree
2 Agree
3 Disagree
4 Strongly disagree

7. On the whole, I am satisfied with myself.
1 Strongly agree
2 Agree
3 Disagree
4 Strongly disagree

8. I feel I am not as good as other people.
1 Strongly agree
2 Agree
3 Disagree
4 Strongly disagree

9. I dislike myself.
1 Strongly agree
2 Agree
3 Disagree
4 Strongly disagree

10. I can't feel proud of the person I am.
1 Strongly agree
2 Agree
3 Disagree
4 Strongly disagree

How to score your Self-Attitude Questionnaire
Transfer the numbers you ringed (your scores) from the Self-Attitude Questionnaire to the spaces opposite. Add the scores in each column, then subtract the total for column two from the total for column one. Add 25 and this gives your self-attitude score.

What your Self-Attitude Score means

Below 14 — you see yourself very positively, as a competent and valuable person. You like and respect yourself, are proud of your achievements, and feel that others approve of you and respect you.

14–16 — you generally have a positive view of yourself. You feel you are as competent as others and that they view you as acceptable and worthwhile.

17–20 — you have an average, fairly balanced view of yourself as having both good and bad points. You feel you can usually hold your own in comparison with others and that other people see you as neither better nor worse than they are.

	Column 1		Column 2
Item		Score	
1	_____		
2	_____		_____
3			_____
4	_____		
5			_____
6	_____		
7	_____		
8			_____
9			_____
10			_____

Total (1) _____   (2) _____

Subtract (2) _____

_____

+ 25

Score _____

21–25 — you tend to be somewhat negative and self-critical. You don't see yourself as being as competent as others and feel that they do not respect you very much.

Above 25 — you generally see yourself very negatively, as less valuable and competent than others. You tend to dislike yourself, 'put yourself down' and feel that others look down on you.

Improving your self-esteem

Is your life dominated by what you 'ought' to do or 'should' be doing, to the point that if you do not live up to these 'oughts' and 'shoulds' you feel guilty, bad and worthless? If this is the case then you may well be suffering from a low self-esteem.

Although living up to our values and beliefs is important, there is a danger that we become obsessive about these and do not allow ourselves to make mistakes or to 'slip-up'. Worse still, we may be living up to not our own beliefs and values but the beliefs and values of others. When this happens we cause ourselves so much discomfort or dissonance that stress and emotional misery are the natural results.

To quote Chandra Patel, 'Healthy values are flexible, modifiable according to current needs, realistic and life-enhancing rather than absolute, global, unrealistic and life-restricting' (Dr Chandra Patel, *The Complete Guide to Stress Management*, Macdonald Optima 1989).

Another thing that can seriously damage our self-esteem is our own inner critical voice. It is the voice in our heads that tells us we are ugly, stupid, incompetent, lazy, greedy and so on. This voice is part of our super-ego or conscience. For some people this critical inner voice can be harsh and unrelenting, and prevents people from seeing themselves in a proper perspective. The slightest mistake means that some people will give themselves a real lashing rather than accept that it is natural to make mistakes, even those that could be avoided.

Our critical inner voice is so much a part of the way that we think that we tend not to notice it, or the damage that it does to us. Psychotherapy is a way of recognising what is going on in our minds and helping us to do something about it. Many women's magazines have articles on self-esteem because it appears that this a problem that particularly affects women. These articles typically run along the lines of '10 ways to improve your self-esteem' or 'How to increase your confidence'. Although they are full of wisdom such as 'treat yourself every day' and 'set yourself achievable objectives', this advice is unlikely to help if your self-esteem really is the pits. Indeed you may feel yourself to be so worthless that you do not deserve psychotherapy. If this is the case then you most definitely do!

Dealing with criticism
Our own critical voice is one thing, but the critical voice of

others is something else again. Whilst most criticism is painful, we can probably bear this if we feel it is constructive and not designed to hurt. Of course, if we are feeling below par anyway we may construe even innocent comments as criticism and feel that others are getting at us. This feeling of persecution is a sign that we are under too much stress. However, it is a fact that some people are very critical and will set out to undermine our self-confidence. Dealing with people like this effectively is important for our own state of well-being.

When people attack us, our first inclination is to defend ourselves, often with a counter-attack. This approach will work in the short-term but is unlikely to fend off your attacker in the long-term as he or she will recognise they have scored a hit by your defensiveness (attack is a form of defence). If we feel intimidated by our attacker we may not respond or may even apologise. This may well make us angry at ourselves as we feel twice wronged, once by the criticism and once by our agreement or collusion with it.

To deal with criticism effectively and assertively takes time to learn but as you become more skilled you will feel the benefits. There are three possible approaches:

— if there is some truth in the criticism, acknowledge this pleasantly but do not apologise (why should you?). An example might be 'Yes, perhaps I should have done that differently';

— agree that there may be some truth in his or her statement without being precise. A typical response might be 'Yes, you could possibly be right';

— if the criticism seems groundless and vague then ask for more information, for instance 'What was it you think I did wrong' or 'Why do you think that'.

In a rather emotional moment I once criticised someone for not caring for me. His response was 'If I don't show I care you think I am criticising you, if I do show I care you try to protect me. What do you want me to do Elaine?' This response was not only a good way of dealing with a criticism without resorting to a counter attack but also gave me feedback as to how I was responding to him. It was also a good example of assertiveness.

ASSERTIVENESS

I would argue very strongly that assertiveness cannot be learnt through a book and so I will not try to teach it.

Assertiveness is a way of dealing with a situation directly and firmly so that neither person comes out feeling attacked. An example that is often used is taking something that is faulty back to a shop and having to deal with a shop assistant and/or manager who refuses to take back the goods. The idea is to make your point clearly and firmly without sounding aggressive and demanding or passive and apologetic.

There are many, many assertiveness training courses available through adult education classes, women's groups, management courses, self-defence courses amongst other options. These courses will make you familiar with your basic assertiveness rights and give you an opportunity through role play to defend these.

Assertive rights

— I have the right to ask for what I want (realising that the other person has a right to say 'No').

— I have the right to an opinion, feelings and emotions and to express them appropriately.

— I have the right to make statements which have no logical basis, and which I do not have to justify.

— I have the right to make my own decisions and cope with the consequences.

— I have the right to choose whether or not to get involved in the problems of someone else.

— I have the right not to know, or to understand, about something.

— I have the right to make mistakes.

— I have the right to be successful.

— I have the right to change my mind.

— I have the right to privacy.

— I have the right to be alone and independent.

— I have the right to change myself and be an assertive person.

Many mental health centres and rehabilitation units run assertiveness training courses for people who use their services. They may also run health promoting assertiveness groups for anybody who would like to go along.

It is equally possible for you to run your own group using the Living Skills Pack, a mental health promotion training pack that gives instructions and exercises in assertiveness. For details on how to get this pack see Useful Addresses below.

It is useful to remember that very few people are confident and assertive in all areas of their lives, although some have become skilled at pretending they are. Deciding to improve your life-skills and doing something about it, whether in stress management, assertiveness, relationship therapy or whatever, is usually a sign of strength and self-awareness and an indication that you are halfway to cracking the problem.

USEFUL ADDRESSES

The Living Skill Pack c/o Dr. Bob Wycherley, District Psychologist, Dept. of Clinical Psychology, Holmesdale House, Hastings, East Sussex.

MIND 22 Harley Street, London, W1. 071 637 0741.

3
HEALTHY BODIES, HEALTHY MINDS

'Well, at least I've got my health'.

The cat may have been run over, the husband unfaithful, the house burnt down, the children delinquent and the milk gone sour — but things could be worse.

Maintaining our mental well-being in modern times is quite an art form, given the pressures on us to indulge in unhealthy pursuits. Over indulging in alcohol and junk food whilst avoiding exercise can all work against our mental well-being, despite the fact many people use them to make themselves feel better. And in the long term, such habits can have serious consequences for our physical and mental health.

ALCOHOL

'The door to alcoholism is not forced open by a determined and suicidal few but lies open and may be inadvertantly entered by any social drinker', writes Jack Lyttle in his book, *Mental Disorder* (Baillière, Tindall, 1986), a warning that is so true.

Despite popular opinion alcohol is, in fact, a depressant, and over-use or abuse can have a devastating effect on an individual and their ability to work and have healthy, happy relationships.

The sooner a drinking problem is recognised, the easier it is to get out from under it. Below are some questions that will help you learn how dependent you may be on alcohol. This is a time to be absolutely honest with yourself — only you can know how seriously you are being hurt by the role alcohol plays in your life.

1. Has someone close to you sometimes expressed concern about your drinking?
2. When faced with a problem, do you often turn to alcohol for relief?
3. Are you sometimes unable to meet home or work responsibilities because of drinking?
4. Have you ever required medical attention as a result of drinking?
5. Have you ever come in conflict with the law in connection with your drinking?
6. Have you often failed to keep promises you have made to yourself about controlling or cutting out your drinking?

If you have answered yes to any of the above questions, your drinking is probably affecting your life in some major ways and you should do something about it — before it gets worse (National Institute on Alcohol Abuse and Alcoholism).

Knowing how much you drink

Considering how long alcohol has been around (almost as long as people) it is surprising how many myths still exist. It is still widely believed that people cannot become alcoholics if they only drink beer, and yet the alcohol content of a half a pint of ordinary strength lager has the same alcohol content as a single (⅙ gill) measure of gin, whisky, vodka or any other spirit; the same alcohol content as a glass of wine, a small glass of sherry or a measure of vermouth or other aperitif. And so statements such as 'I can drink lager all night and it has no effect on me, but I get really drunk on whisky' need to be examined closely. For a guideline as to how much alcohol is in each drink and how much is considered safe, read on:

Alcohol units per drink

		Unit
BEERS AND LAGERS		
Ordinary strength beer or lager	½ pint	1
	1 pint	2
	1 can	1½
Export beer	1 pint	2½
	1 can	2
Strong ale or lager	½ pint	2½
	1 pint	4
	1 can	3
Extra strength beer or lager	½ pint	2½
	1 pint	5
	1 can	4
CIDERS		
Average cider	½ pint	1½
	1 pint	3
	Quart bottle	6
Strong cider	½ pint	2
	1 pint	4
	Quart bottle	8

SPIRITS

	Unit
1 standard single measure in most of England and Wales (⅙ gill)	1
1 standard single measure in Northern Ireland (¼ gill)	1½
⅕ gill measure	1¼
¼ gill measure served in some parts of Scotland	1½
1 bottle	30

TABLE WINE (including cider wine and barley wine)
1 standard glass	1
1 bottle	7
1 litre bottle	10

SHERRY AND FORTIFIED WINE
1 standard small measure	1
1 bottle	12

How much should you drink?

From a mental health viewpoint the question of what is a 'safe' amount of alcohol to drink is a slightly complicated one to answer. The recommended 'sensible' limit according to the Health Education Authority is up to 21 units a week for men and up to 14 units a week for women but spread throughout the week. This allows for two or three enjoyable evenings out with friends without seriously damaging your liver! However, if you are sitting at home or alone in a bar miserably drinking, say four gin and tonics or three pints of beer, then you are in danger of an increased risk of depression.

This is because although alcohol acts as a stimulant at first, it is in fact a depressant and will act upon the central nervous system in a way that will lower, rather than elevate your mood, as well as affecting your judgement, skills and self-control.

DIET

The importance of diet is underplayed in all aspects of mental health, except where it is part of an obvious problem, such as anorexia. Yet diet can play a major part in mental health matters in many ways. Some foods and drinks, for instance, give your metabolic system quite a jolt. Coffee is well known for containing the stimulant caffeine, but it is perhaps less well known that tea, soft drinks, particularly of the cola variety, chocolate, sugar, salt and man-made food (E) additives can also stimulate the mind and body. In short, some foods can be mood affecting. Tension, fatigue and irritability can also be caused by the consumption of large quantities of sugar, and salt increases nervous tension, fluid retention and the level of your blood pressure.

Given that these foodstuffs can cause these reactions in someone whose mental health is fine, imagine the problems they could cause for someone who is already suffering from anxiety. They would seriously exacerbate their existing symptoms.

If you find that your mood does alter after meals containing certain foodstuffs you could run a home trial to see if the pattern repeats itself if you have the same food-stuffs on a regular basis. Try varying your diet, particularly including raw vegetables and fruit, and see how this improves your feeling of well-being.

If you are unsure as to whether or not your diet is considered healthy, then ask your GP for advice. He or she may well refer you to the health authority dietician. However the generally accepted advice is to avoid 'junk' foods and high-calorie snacks, despite the short-term energy high that they may give you. Also avoid eating a diet with a high proportion of animal fats and dairy products, and try where possible to increase your intake of raw vegetables and fruits as well as pulses. You will find that after a time on a more healthy diet, your system will feel noticeably sluggish if you return to a burgers and chips type menu for even a day.

It is now widely suggested that foodstuffs with a range of additives should be avoided as they can cause reactions in some people, such as the well-publicised hyperactivity in children. It is recommended that the main additives to avoid are tartrazine and related food colourings. The main E numbers to be avoided are: E102, 104, 107, 110, 122, 123, 128, 151, 154, 155 and 180. Some E numbers, however, are natural colourings, such as those numbered from E160 to E170. In some products the E numbers are not displayed and so it might be best to avoid products with additives or preservatives if you have any suspicion that these may be causing you problems.

Organic foodstuffs are expensive and sometimes look limp and rather unattractive on display. However they are usually much better in nutritional terms. If you cannot afford to purchase organic foods or your local shops do not stock them, then if you have a garden, even a small one, you may find it worth learning organic gardening methods and producing your own healthy fruit and vegetables. If all of these options are out of the question, then the following basic rules may give you a guide to cutting down your intake of questionable substances:

- Always scrub fruit and vegetables that are to be eaten unpeeled, and wash salad stuffs thoroughly.
- Although much of the goodness lies just beneath the skin of root vegetables, peeling these will help you get rid of some of the absorbed pesticides and chemical residues.
- Filter your water. There are many types of water filter now available, some more sophisticated than others, but some are relatively cheap and well worth the investment.

Eating a low-fat diet, avoiding red meat, eating a good intake of fibre and including a good proportion of fruit and vegetables (uncooked or steamed) is well recognised as important to over-all well-being.

Self-regulation of eating

Sometimes our problem is not just that we eat the wrong things but that we eat too much. This can affect both our physical and mental health to varying degrees. In the extreme an eating disorder known as bulimia can develop (see pp. 16–17). If you feel that food is playing too dominant a role in your life, it might be useful to monitor your eating patterns and intake, so that you can take more control over it. Do this by keeping a daily log which details everything you eat. Note the amount eaten, the type of food and calorific value, the time of day and, last but certainly not least, the circumstances of eating. This record will establish the calorie intake that is maintaining your present weight. It will also help to identify the stimuli that elicit and reinforce your eating behaviour, eg it may show that you eat when you are bored rather than when you are hungry.

At the same time, construct a weight chart for yourself. Decide how much you want to lose overall and set a weekly goal for weight loss. Your weekly goal should be realistic (between 1 and 2 pounds). Record your weight each day on graph paper. In addition to showing how your weight varies with food intake, this visual record will reinforce your dieting efforts as you observe progress towards your goal.

What might help
Follow these guidelines to help you control your eating.

- Eat only at a specific time and in a specific place. Do not eat at other times or in other places (eg while standing in the kitchen).
- Do not combine eating with other activities, such as reading or watching television.
- Do not keep fattening or other unhealthy foodstuffs in the house.
- Shop for food only after having had a full meal; but only those items that are on a previously prepared list.
- Eat meals very slowly, paying close attention to the food.
- Finish chewing and swallowing each mouthful before putting more food on the fork.
- Put your knife and fork down occasionally before continuing to eat.

If you find yourself tempted to eat at times other than those specified, do something that is incompatible with eating. For example, exercise to music, go for a walk, talk with a friend (preferably one who knows you are dieting), study your diet plan and weight graph, noting how much weight you have lost.

Equally important, reward yourself with an activity you

Desired weight table according to height and frame
(Indoor clothing without shoes)

WEIGHT

| HEIGHT | Small Frame | | Medium Frame | | Large Frame | |
	Women	Men	Women	Men	Women	Men
ft in	st lb	st lb	st lb	st lb	st lb	st lb
4 10	7 3	—	7 8	—	8 4	—
4 11	7 4	—	7 11	—	8 8	—
5 0	7 7	—	8 1	—	8 10	—
5 1	7 11	8 3	8 3	8 12	8 13	9 7
5 2	8 0	8 6	8 6	9 0	9 3	9 10
5 3	8 2	8 9	8 11	9 4	9 7	9 13
5 4	8 6	8 12	9 0	9 7	9 11	10 3
5 5	8 11	9 2	9 4	9 10	10 0	10 7
5 6	8 13	9 6	9 9	10 0	10 5	10 10
5 7	9 3	9 10	9 13	10 5	10 9	11 1
5 8	9 8	10 0	10 4	10 9	10 13	11 5
5 9	9 12	10 5	10 6	10 13	11 3	11 10
5 10	10 3	10 9	10 10	11 3	11 7	12 1
5 11	10 6	10 13	11 0	11 8	11 10	12 6
6 0	—	11 3	—	11 12	—	12 10
6 1	—	11 7	—	12 3	—	13 0
6 2	—	11 12	—	12 8	—	13 6
6 3	—	12 0	—	12 12	—	13 12

enjoy (watching television, reading, planning a new wardrobe, visiting a friend) when you have followed your plan for a day. Plan larger rewards (for example, buying yourself something you want) for a specified amount of weight loss. Self-punishment (other than foregoing a reward) will only make you miserable and should be avoided.

EXERCISE

We all have a thousand and one excuses for not taking exercise: I'm too tired, it's boring, I haven't got time, I haven't got the energy, I'm no good at sport, I'm not fit enough (well of course you're not, you don't take enough exercise!), I need to lose weight first (you need to burn up calories by taking exercise!). But it is a fact of life that exercise is essential for our well-being, and that goes for our mental health as well as our physical health.

Exercise works to improve our physical and mental well-being by:

- toning up our bodies and making us look healthier and therefore more attractive, which in turn helps us to feel good about ourselves;
- making us feel less tired by improving the efficiency of our heart and circulatory system;
- stimulating chemicals in our bodies that give us a 'lift', making us feel more positive and less depressed;
- improving our appetite and digestion;
- strengthening our bodies, our minds and our confidence;
- providing an outlet for tension and frustration and helping us to relax;
- giving us a feeling of healthy tiredness and helping us sleep better;
- helping to prevent physical illnesses, such as heart disease and osteoporosis (bone-thinning, a major cause of fractures and deaths in the elderly, particularly women).

There are many different forms of exercise and any exercise is better than none. For example, there is walking, running, playing team games, badminton, swimming, aerobics, dancing, yoga, tennis, bowls, golf, weight-training, martial arts, cycling, squash, rowing — this list goes on and on.

Perhaps the first criteria to bear in mind when considering taking up exercise are safety, suitability and satisfaction.

Safety

It is very important that you don't attempt too strenuous an activity if you are not very fit. Either your GP or a reputable health and leisure instructor, perhaps at your local health centre, can assess your current level of fitness and give you some indication of the type of exercise it would be safe for you to start with. Swimming, for instance, is excellent for building up suppleness, stamina and strength without placing too great a strain on the heart, whereas trying to run or jog a few miles when over-weight, out of condition and without guidelines on how to warm up your muscles first will only result in problems that could have long-term consequences.

Be kind to yourself. Accept it will take time and perseverance to reach a satisfactory level of fitness, and that you might experience a small amount of aches and pains in the beginning. The general advice is a little at a time, building up slowly and gently until you reach peak fitness again.

Suitability and satisfaction

Exercise should fit into your lifestyle and not dominate it. A busy mother at home with children may be lucky enough to have a local aerobics group with a crêche or a supportive friend or relative. However if these things are not available, a home exercise programme available on videos, in books or even on audio-cassette (tape) might be a solution, as might home exercise equipment which can take the form of stationary bikes, rowing machines, weights and even 'mini-gyms'. Elderly people obviously need to watch what they tackle, but there is still a good range of activities that are possible. Swimming, brisk walking and bowls, for instance, all provide a level of exercise that will vastly improve well-being. As fitness improves for all age ranges, other more energetic activities might be attempted.

If you really hate jogging, then there is little point in forcing yourself out there on the streets, pounding tarmac for hours on end. Start from the point of what you might enjoy most.

Suppleness, stamina and strength

Exercise works to build up the three 'S's' — suppleness, stamina and strength.

Suppleness is important as exercise can place a strain

on your muscles, ligaments and tendons. If these are not supple or pliable then you are far more likely to experience aches and pains. Gentle stretching should be a part of any exercise programme and a precursor to any sport.

If you have had to run for a bus recently, then you will have some idea of your level of stamina. Stamina is your ability to keep going without having to stop to 'catch' your breath. If you have to sprint for a bus and it takes several minutes before your breathing gets back to normal then your stamina level may well need building up.

In order to meet some of the physical demands placed upon us, such as lifting children, moving furniture or even protecting ourselves, it is necessary to build up our strength. By using light weights or weight machines on a carefully designed programme it is possible to build up not just our strength but also to improve our muscle tone, making us look younger and fitter.

Motivation

All the opportunity in the world is of no use if your motivation to improve your physical fitness is not there.

Some people are enormously motivated towards physical fitness. You may well see them out jogging in the pouring rain or thrashing around a squash court in a heatwave. However, most of us experience peaks and troughs in our motivation to do most things, even the things we really enjoy, particularly if these things take effort. Eating a cream cake, having a drink or smoking a cigarette are reasonably effortless ways to make ourselves feel better, albeit temporarily, and although the long-term consequences of all three might be negative and even life-threatening (obesity, drink-related health problems and cancer), there is still a tendency on many people's parts to take the 'easy' route.

If your motivation to take exercise is really very low most of the time, then it might help to set up a positive reward system for yourself. For instance, allow yourself a long lie in bed on the Sunday if you have exercised for half an hour on the Saturday.

GETTING A GOOD NIGHT'S SLEEP

Sleeplessness (insomnia) or restless nights can be a source of a great deal of distress for many people. An easy answer might seem to be to turn to sleeping tablets (hypnotics). However, drug-induced sleep is not as healthy nor refreshing as a deep natural sleep and so it is well worth trying other methods first, only turning to medication as a last resort and then only for as short a time as possible.

The main indication that you have a sleeping problem is if you feel tired and unrefreshed first thing in the morning. If this is the case, then you need to understand what might be causing the sleeping problem.

Early waking, between the hours of 3 o'clock and 5 o'clock in the morning, is an indication of depression, particularly if other symptoms are present (see Chapter 1). Difficulty in getting to sleep at night may well be a sign of anxiety (see Chapter 1). However, there may be no underlying cause, but very practical reasons that can be dealt with easily once understood.

Age — to begin with, as we grow older we simply need less sleep as we become less active.

Activity — the less active we are the less we tend to tire ourselves (although boredom can be exhausting). Try to think of a time when you have engaged in a physically tiring activity like playing squash, running or gardening and remember how sleepy you felt, particularly after a relaxing bath or a glass of wine (one tot will relax you and help you sleep, more than this may add to your sleep problems). Intellectual activities are also very tiring but we can find it difficult to switch our minds off, causing tension and difficulty in sleeping. If you find that your mind is racing with ideas and problems chasing each other around in your head, then try writing your thoughts down on paper.

Noise — traffic, noisy neighbours or a snoring partner can sometimes make sleep impossible. Not only does the noise keep us awake but so does the tension we experience as we get increasingly irritated and anxious about feeling too tired to face the next day's agenda. If you cannot do anything about the source of the problem then earplugs might prove to be an answer.

Discomfort — an uncomfortable mattress may be something you have become used to but may well be causing you more problems than you realise.

Sleep disruption can be a major source of anxiety and vice-versa.

Sleeping tablets may be an answer in the short-term but for both a healthy body and a healthy mind understanding and dealing with the causes of sleeplessness will often bring the greatest rewards.

STAYING WELL

Keeping ourselves well is sometimes very difficult given the pressures of twentieth century living. However, there are plenty of sources of advice — magazines, T.V., GPs, health visitors — the list is endless.

What is more difficult to deal with are issues like homelessness, poverty, disability and other things seemingly beyond our control. To tackle these threats to health it is often necessary to work with others, for instance as a member of a pressure group. Your local Citizen's Advice Bureau or Voluntary Services Group should have a list of local groups and organisations.

4
GROWING GOOD?
— A GUIDE TO
THERAPY

Our minds are an invisible amalgamation of our emotions, thoughts, spirits, experiences and body chemistry.

Ideally, all these components should allow the mind to develop at an even pace, and our absolute mental health would then benefit enormously. Our body chemistry, for instance, would have a little more respect for the fact that our emotions are not as objective or functional as our neurotransmitters and would give them some time to catch up. During adolescence, when our hormones become manic, racing around our bodies in a state of euphoria, issuing instructions willy-nilly regardless of the consequences, our emotions might have got as far as nipping down to the library of our experiences to get some good reliable data and arranging a meeting to decide how to deal with the changes. But at this point thought intervenes, just to add to the confusion. Rather than going by the appropriate channels and doing a bit of background research, 'thought' tends to drop in on 'experience' for little more than a gossip and then, more often than not, acts. Never mind having a quiet word with our emotions or some respect for our spirit. Oh no. Thought tends to be a bit maverick and egotistical. How often have we heard those words: 'I, thought. It was the right thing to do!'

Conspicuous imbalances occur at different times in our lives. Adolescence, the male and female menopause and a woman's monthly cycle create imbalances that can often seriously disrupt a person's life and cause a great deal of misery. These are examples where our body chemistry is leading our emotions a merry dance. Our emotions, however, are quite capable of calling the tune.

These imbalances, or as they are more often referred to, stresses, can be stimulated by events, such as marriage, the birth of a baby, the loss of someone close to you, moving house, or a change in your job status. Stress is dealt with in much greater detail in Chapter 2, but the associated imbalance in lifestyle or focus in our lives is the issue here.

There are also times when the finely tuned balance of our emotions, our body chemistry, is upset, but in a way that we are a long way from understanding. For example, mental health problems that are grouped under the term schizophrenia (see Chapter 1) are explained in a variety of ways, from disease of the brain to the result of complicated and difficult family communications.

For many years, mental health problems have been treated by drugs (chemotherapy). For the more severe instances, drug treatment still plays a major part of a patient's care. However, drug treatment for mild to moderate depression and anxiety has lost a great deal of favour over the past few years. In its place has come an increasing emphasis on psychotherapy. This approach allows someone to talk through their problems and related issues with a trained therapist, with the aim of helping them achieve a greater understanding of themselves, their strengths and weaknesses, the situation they are in, and assisting them to find their own solutions. People may work on a one-to-one basis or in a group situation.

However there are many different approaches to psychotherapy and some approaches may suit one person's needs better than another. Not all mental health problems are best treated by talking issues through. In some instances it is the situation and not the individual that should change. There are times when legal, economic or political change are the only real solution and as important as our ability to come to terms with the iniquities in life.

However for many people, therapy can be a positive, strengthening force.

CHOOSING THERAPY

I'm afraid of the therapist, I want help, but I don't know whether to trust him. He might see things which I don't know in myself — frightening and bad elements. He seems not to be judging me, but I'm sure he is. I can't tell him what really concerns me, but I can tell him about some past experiences that are related to my concern. He seems to understand those, so I can reveal a bit more of myself.

But now I've shared with him some of this bad side of me, he despises me. I'm sure of it, but it's strange I can find little evidence of it. Do you suppose that what I've told him isn't so bad? Is it possible that I need not be ashamed of it as a part of me? I no longer feel that he despises me. It makes me feel that I want to go further, exploring me, perhaps expressing more of myself. I find him a sort of companion as I do this — he seems really to understand.

But now I'm getting frightened again, and this time deeply frightened. I didn't realise that exploring the unknown recesses of myself would make me feel feelings I've never experienced before. It's very strange because in one way these aren't new feelings. I sense that they've always been there. But they seem so bad and disturbing I've never dared to let them flow in me. And now as I live these feelings in the hours with him, I feel terribly shaky, as though my world is falling apart. It used to be sure and firm. Now it is loose, permeable and vulnerable. It isn't pleasant to feel things I've always been frightened of before. It's his fault, yet curiously I'm eager to see him and I feel more safe when I'm with him.

I don't know who I am any more, but sometimes when I feel things I seem solid and real for a moment. I'm troubled by the contradictions I find in myself — I act one way and feel another — I think one thing and feel another. It is very disconcerting. It's also sometimes adventurous and exhilarating to be trying to discover who I am. Sometimes I catch myself feeling that perhaps the person I am is worth being, whatever that means.

I'm beginning to find it very satisfying, though often painful, to share just what it is I'm feeling at this moment. You know, it is really helpful to try to listen to myself, to hear what is going on in me. I'm not so frightened any more of what is going on in me. It seems pretty trustworthy, I use some of my hours with him to dig deep into myself to know what I am feeling. It's scary work, but I want to know, and I do trust him most of the time, and that helps. I feel pretty vulnerable and raw, but I know he doesn't want to hurt me, and I even believe he cares. It occurs to me as I try to let myself down and down, deep into myself, that maybe if I could sense what is going on in me, and could realise its meaning, I would know who I am, and I would also know what to do. At least I feel this knowing sometimes with him.

I can even tell him just how I'm feeling toward him at any given moment, and instead of this killing the relationship, as I used to fear, it seems to deepen it. Do you suppose I could be my feelings with other people also? Perhaps that wouldn't be too dangerous either.

You know, I feel as if I'm floating along on the current of life, very adventurously, being me. I get defeated sometimes, I get hurt sometimes, but I'm learning that those experiences are not fatal. I don't know exactly who I am, but I can feel my reactions at any given moment, and they seem to work out pretty well as a basis for my behaviour from moment to moment. Maybe this is what it means to be me. But of course I can only do this because I feel safe in the relationship with my therapist. Or could I be myself this way outside of this relationship? I wonder, I wonder. Perhaps I could.

Carl Rogers *On Personal Power*, pp. 12–14

This passage gives a beautiful and honest insight into what psychotherapy can offer someone who has a need to understand themselves, their hurts, their lives and their potential more fully, as a way forward in their lives.

When it comes to choosing a therapy, there is a growing feeling that the choice of therapist is as important, if not more so, than the type of therapy employed. Certainly when it comes to evaluating the outcome of various types of psychotherapies there is little hard evidence that promotes one approach over another, and so choosing a 'most' effective therapy is going to be to some extent the luck of the draw.

THE PSYCHOTHERAPIES

Psychotherapy is a means of dealing with mental health issues by trying to help the patient understand and deal with the thoughts, emotions and behaviour involved in their difficulties, rather than by merely treating the symptoms with medication or other more interventionist means such as ECT (electro-convulsive therapy — see Chapter 7, Drug Treatments and their Alternatives). There are a wide variety of therapeutic techniques. I describe these below in the order that I have understood them rather than by any other means (such as effectiveness or preference).

Counselling

There is no hard and fast distinction between counselling and psychotherapy. In general use, counselling is a talking therapy that allows people to deal with specific life issues, such as relationship difficulties or career changes, while psychotherapy is used to deal with 'deeper' issues, usually with people whose past experiences are causing them problems in the here and now and which need to be explored and dealt with. However, it might be difficult to think of a 'deeper' issue than that of relationships. And the fact that the relationship difficulty might have resulted in a broken marriage for one person or a schizophrenic-type illness for another should not determine the difference between counselling or psychotherapy, although the therapist should be experienced in their respective client areas.

Perhaps the best distinction is suggested by E. Bordin

(*Psychological Counselling*, New York, Appleton-Century-Crofts, 1955) who suggests that counselling refers to psychological interventions that deal with rational, conscious factors while psychotherapy works with affective or unconscious factors.

Both counselling and psychotherapy are very different from analytical or interpretative psychotherapies (such as dream analysis).

Psychoanalysis

Psychoanalysis was the first formally developed method of psychotherapy. Developed by Sigmund Freud, psychoanalysis concentrates upon the mental health problems that develop as a result of a battle between our inbuilt aggressive and sexual impulses (what Freud called the 'id') and our learnt need to hold these impulses in (our 'ego' and 'superego'). This internal battle, according to Freud, starts in early childhood and may have the effect of preventing a person from being able to cope effectively with relationships and the pressures created by his or her environment.

Repressed sexual and aggressive feelings are, for psychoanalysts, at the root of neurosis. Analysis and the consequent understanding of repressed fears, it is believed, allows the individual to deal with the issues involved. The guiding principle of psychoanalysis is free association. With free association a patient (or client as they may more often be called) is encouraged by the analyst to give free rein to their thoughts and feelings. That is, to say whatever comes into their heads without censorship. Where a patient feels this to be impossible they should admit to the censorship, as this is a valid part of unblocking thoughts and emotions. Imagine, just for a minute what repeating out loud exactly what comes into your head might entail saying: 'Why is he asking me to say whatever comes into my head? I don't see the point. Stupid man. And he is so ugly. Expensive too. I haven't collected the damn laundry yet. It always rains on Tuesdays.' From such free association the analyst will attempt to break down blockages or resistance in thoughts and feelings and then encourage interpretation. The idea behind this approach is that the patient is helped to discover issues of personal but hitherto unidentified importance.

The patient's relationship with the analyst is an important part of the approach. During psychoanalysis, the analyst always sits out of view of the client or patient. As the relationship develops, the patient begins to respond to the analyst in particular ways. For instance, a patient may feel very warmly toward the analyst or, alternatively, he or she may feel very hostile. Freud referred to this as transference. His assumption was that transference was an indication of feelings for significant others, such as parents, which are transferred to the analyst. This transference is important and should be worked on.

As the analysis continues patients experience therapeutic benefit through:

- abreaction
- insight
- working through

Abreaction is a term that describes the release of very strong emotions, such as anger. This may come as a result of talking about painful past experiences. The process of abreaction does not take away the memory of the original experience, but can provide a release for bottled-up emotions and also the opportunity to discover more.

The continuous exploration of experience and emotion can lead to a gradual insight into the source of the problems the patient is experiencing. Once this insight has been achieved it is a case of helping the patient to understand and change his or her responses in situations where they may be experiencing particular difficulty. This is referred to as 'working through'.

Psychoanalysis, like many of the psychoanalytic psychotherapies, aims to work through neuroses, and therefore is felt to be unsuitable for people experiencing a psychotic disturbance, compulsive disorders (see Behaviour

Therapy below) or addictions.

Psychoanalysis is expensive. In most cases it entails at least three sessions a week, and psychoanalysts, who have themselves been through psychoanalysis, are not cheap. If you have the money and are interested in this type of approach then you can acquire a list of qualified practitioners from the British Association of Psychotherapists.

Psychoanalysis is not available on the NHS.

Psychoanalytic psychotherapy
Based on the principles of psychoanalysis, psychoanalytic psychotherapy differs in four fundamental ways:

- The therapist is in full view of the client.
- The client is unlikely to be lying down on a couch, but rather sitting on a chair facing the therapist.
- The therapist concentrates on actual life problems rather than meandering through the unconscious.
- The therapist places less emphasis on the biological drives and more on the social and cultural factors that shape our lives and behaviour.

However, in a similar way to psychoanalysis, psychoanalytic psychotherapy is based on the belief that unconscious motives and fears are what lie beneath most emotional problems.

Neo-Freudian analysis
There are a number of so-called neo-Freudian schools of thought in the psychoanalytic field. Led by notable personalities such as Adler, Fromm Horney, Rank and Sullivan, these schools place less emphasis on Freud's libido theory (the premise of which is that people are driven by instinctual drives) and more on culture and the importance of interpersonal relationships. They acknowledge the importance of security and self-esteem to the individual.

Jungian psychotherapy
Jung preferred to refer to his approach as analytical

psychology rather than psychoanalysis. For him the unconscious was not just unique to each individual, tied to the growth, development and experiences of that individual, the unconscious was also shared, constituting a common 'inherited' knowledge. This he referred to as the 'collective unconscious'. Jung's beliefs therefore took him beyond Freud, in that Freud believed that repressed experiences (during this lifetime) are what shapes our actions while Jung looked to deeper, transpersonal influences.

Dream analysis to Jung was a way of getting in touch with this collective unconscious, a way of contacting mythical archetypes or original models of ourselves. It is the active exploration of this symbolism that underpins Jungian psychotherapy. For Jung neurosis is an attempt at self-cure and madness a struggle to achieve greater insight or understanding.

Post-analytic one-to-one therapies

Gestalt therapy   Although the founder of Gestalt therapy, Frederick (Fritz) Perls, was himself once a Freudian who trained analysts, anything less like psychoanalysis than Gestalt therapy might be hard to come by.

In contrast to psychoanalysis, Gestalt therapy is grounded very much in the 'here and now' — that is, there is no exploration of the past. The emphasis is on awareness of what the individual wants and needs *now.* The emphasis is also on feeling. Unlike the talking psychotherapies, Gestalt therapy places far more emphasis on the whole person. The body, how it moves and feels are seen as just as important as the mind, its thoughts and verbal expressions.

Exploration of feelings is often done dramatically. For example, a client might be asked by a Gestalt therapist to role play, alternatively, themselves and a member of their family with whom they may have some unfinished business (unresolved conflict). They may do this by using an empty chair which they will address as if the other party is sitting there.

Primal therapy Dr Arthur Janov's primal therapy is based on the belief that deeply painful childhood experiences remain with us and that it is the childish fending off of this pain and the subsequent long-lasting tension that creates the neurosis that stays with us. For Janov the need is to uproot this deep-seated pain and literally scream it out.

The way in which primal therapy works, or at least how it is structured, is different from most other types of talking therapies. It involves the patient in removing themselves from their ordinary lives for a period of three weeks, either by moving into a hotel or therapy centre. They are to take no drugs, including alcohol and cigarettes, which might ordinarily be used to reduce tension. The patient has a session with a therapist each day for this period. The sessions are not defined by any time limit and may go on for several hours or until the therapist decides that the patient has had enough.

In each session the therapist works towards getting the patient to express their deepest feelings towards their parents. The concentration on the basic fear and pain, centred around the patient's belief that they were unloved by their parents and the trauma that caused, is intended to cut out the transference so important in psychoanalysis. The simple truth, as perceived by Dr Janov, is that re-experiencing those early feelings will get rid of both the neurosis and the associated transference.

Following the initial three week session, clients can continue in a primal group which does not act in the same way as other group therapies (see below), but is rather a cluster of individuals pursuing their own primal experience rather than contributing to the group and the growth of the other participants.

Rogerian therapy Rogerian therapy is the embodiment of the humanist approach to psychotherapy. The Rogerian world view is a very positive one, believing that people are essentially positive, whole beings and that therapy can bring this wholeness, this good feeling, to the surface.

The belief is that the therapy works by talking things through with a therapist who is non-judgemental and who should hold the patient in unconditional, positive regard, the regard being for what the person essentially is rather than what he or she says or does. It is essential that the therapist's responses to the client are sincere.

The therapist works in a one-to-one situation by feeding back to the patient the words or statements that hold a key to how the patient feels about something. The idea is to help the client become aware of their self-perception which is laced with self-hatred and, through the continued positive regard of the therapist, to see themselves in a more loving, accepting light.

The Rogerian therapeutic approach is one that is increasingly being developed and used amongst mental health professionals in this country, particularly mental health nurses

Biofunctional therapy Biofunctional therapists believe that neurosis stems from a disruption in the body's ability to function naturally. Therapists use a variety of approaches including massage and movement to re-establish this natural functioning.

Hypnotherapy Hypnotherapy is associated with 'putting people to sleep' (altering their state of consciousness) and then instigating behavioural changes. As a therapy it is used to tackle certain addictions like smoking and gambling. However, hypnotherapy can also be used in a much more subtle way, by inducing a trance-like state (there is no loss of consciousness) that allows the mind to wander, but in a gently directed way. As an exercise it can be very therapeutic.

Behaviour and cognitive behaviour therapies
Behavioural therapies are distinct from other types in three main ways:

- The individual's 'problem' is seen as being distinct

from them as a person; rather it is something separate from them but something that they 'own', or agree that they have, such as a fear of flying in aeroplanes.

• Using methods based on learning theories, behaviour therapy is directive rather than suggestive.

• It claims to be scientific in as much as its methods and results are observable, measurable, testable and reproducible.

There has been a huge growth in the credibility and use of behaviour therapy to treat many mental health problems and behaviour therapists claim something like a 90 per cent success rate. However, although this looks very impressive on paper it must be remembered that behaviour therapists select their clients on the basis of their suitability for behaviour therapy, which must improve their chances of success enormously.

Behaviour therapy is not designed to help the client understand why he or she is behaving in a particular way, but to change the existing behaviour by retraining, by learning more appropriate behaviours in given situations.

There are several techniques used by behaviour therapists and these should be selected according to the individual patient's needs.

Assertiveness training This is now so popular, it is probably not recognised by many people as being a form of behaviour therapy. However, it is widely used to help people deal with difficult everyday situations, such as dealing with an awkward boss, taking faulty goods back to a shop and generally helping us assert ourselves when faced with a person or situation that can be adverse for our general mental health.

Aversion therapy The aim of this technique is to get the patient to associate their unwanted behaviour with an unpleasant experience. A simple example that many parents have probably tried is painting a child's nails with bitter almonds in an attempt to stop a nail-biting habit.

Giving someone with an alcohol problem a drug called Antabuse which makes them feel very sick if they drink alcohol is another example. Obviously the patient or client's consent to this type of treatment is essential to its success.

Contracts This is simply an agreement between two or more people to try and change some behaviour pattern. Success or failure is discussed with the therapist at following sessions.

Desensitisation This is often used in situations where a person has an exaggerated fear of something, such as flying or spiders. The person is helped to relax and then is very gently and gradually exposed to what he or she fears. In the case of a fear of spiders, the person may initially be shown a photograph of a spider, followed by a toy spider. This process would continue until the person felt able to be confronted by and even touch a real spider. This gradual exposure is very different to flooding or implosion.

Flooding or implosion With this method a person is (with his or her consent) confronted with his or her fear and is then assisted to deal with the feelings of anxiety or panic that follow. For instance, someone with a fear of open spaces would be taken to the middle of a very large field, and someone with a fear of spiders would probably have several dumped in his or her lap. It is hoped that in this way the person will learn that they will survive the event with (hopefully) no lasting ill-effects. This approach is more popular in the United States than in the United Kingdom, although its popularity is waning.

Modelling In this approach the therapist models the desired behaviour.

Operant conditioning This is a sort of opposite to aversion therapy, whereby a person is rewarded for 'good' behaviour. For someone suffering from anorexia, this type of approach is used to encourage eating, as the desired behaviour, ie eating food, is rewarded with increased or returned privileges. Parents often use operant conditioning to motivate children to behave well, particularly in public.

Paradoxical intention This works in a rather peculiar way, as the patient is encouraged to produce the symptom, such as anxiety, and then told to make it worse. This has the paradoxical effect of getting rid of the symptom.

Group therapy

As many people find that their greatest difficulties lie in the way they relate to other people, it can be of particular benefit to work through some of these difficulties in a group therapy setting.

The therapeutic factors are believed to be:

- Acceptance — the sense of belonging, being supported, cared for and valued by the group; in particular, being accepted even when someone has revealed something about themselves which they themselves regarded as unacceptable. This factor is especially important in early stages of group membership.
- Self-disclosure — revealing previously hidden personal information about oneself to the group. Not to be equated with high participation or with dramatic openness.
- Catharsis — the emotional release leading to relief by ventilating feelings (positive or negative) about life events or other group members.
- Learning from interpersonal actions — making an effort to relate in a constructive way to the group, either by initiating some behaviour or responding to other group members. The person's attempt to change his way of relating is more important than the reactions of the other members.
- Self-understanding (insight) — the person learns something important about his behaviour, his assumptions or his motivations. This can come about through

feedback, confrontation or interpretation by the rest of the group.

- Universality — seeing that other group members have similar problems and feelings, reducing the person's sense of being unique or alone.
- Altruism — the person feels better about himself because he learns that he can be of value to others; he improves his own self-image by helping other group members.
- Vicarious learning — the person experiences something of value for himself by observing other group members.
- Guidance — the person receives useful factual information or instruction from the group leader, or advice and suggestions from other group members.
- Instillation of hope — seeing that other members improve gives the person a sense of optimism about his own potential for progress.

Family therapy

Most therapies concentrate on the individual, working with them to discover and deal with various 'blocks' to personal development and growth. However, it was recognised that while individual therapy seemed to have a beneficial effect for many people, they sometimes experienced a relapse or re-experience of old problems once they returned to their family settings. This, along with the growing interest in 'systems', led to the development of family therapy.

In the family therapy setting, brothers, sisters, mother and father are all included. In fact, some therapists like to include the extended family, and so grandparents and even aunts and uncles can be involved.

The belief behind family therapy is that the mental health problems shown by the person who has become the patient is only a sign that there is something not operating in an ideal way within the family. In other words, it is the family system that is causing the problem.

The way in which family therapy works is quite complex

and may seem very threatening to those involved. The family sits in a room with a therapist who will question actions and reactions of various family members. However, because the therapist, albeit temporarily, becomes involved in the system, there needs to be independent observers who can watch the whole proceedings without being in the same room and therefore affecting proceedings. The way this is accomplished is to have a large two-way mirror in the therapy room through which the observers can see what is going on. They are able to talk to the therapist in the room and suggest questions that he or she might ask of one or more of the family.

All this is, of course, carried out with the full co-operation of family members, who are involved to the point of agreeing to the members of the team who will act as observers.

In other situations, the family may work with two therapists, usually a male and female, in the family home. It is also possible for therapists to videotape the family during their therapy session in order to allow family members to witness second-hand certain important, perhaps destructive, interactions.

Family therapy is believed to be of particular benefit to people who suffer from a schizophrenic-type mental health problem.

Marital therapy

'Marital' therapy is now an outdated term as more and more people set up long-term relationships outside the marriage bond. This has been recognised by the largest relationship counselling organisation in the UK, Relate, who used to go under the title of Marriage Guidance Council.

For couple counselling to be successful, both partners need to be involved. Although approaches differ, the main emphasis is on getting partners to gain more understanding of each others needs, to help them communicate their feelings more effectively to each other and to find effective strategies for resolving their conflicts.

Sex therapy and psycho-sexual counselling

This is usually, but not always, a specialist area of relation-ship therapy. The reason I say 'usually but not always' is because there is a tendency to overlook the fact that people outside an intimate relationship may have a need for therapy, say if they are experiencing some difficulty in coming to terms with their sexuality and how this expresses itself. This therapy is offered in the form of psycho-sexual counselling.

Self-help groups

One of the biggest mistakes I made as a struggling single parent through the 1970s was not to join a self-help group. For some reason I felt there was a virtue in coping by myself. Support, sharing, understanding, information and care — these are the things offered by self-help groups. And they are things, like it or not, that we all need. However, admitting it can sometimes be hard.

There are self-help groups that have come together for a multitude of reasons, to meet a multitude of needs. Alco-holics Anonymous, perhaps the most well known, has over a million members. One of the worst feelings when you are suffering from any mental health problem, be it loneliness, alcoholism, depression or a schizophrenic-type illness, is that you are alone. Because of the fear and ignorance that exists around mental health problems, gaining support from your local community or even some of your friends may prove very difficult. In any case, if the people around you have not had your experience it may prove very diffi-cult for them to empathise and be supportive. Depressed people may be told to pull themselves together. Unless someone suffers with alcoholism, they may find it impos-sible to understand the craving for drink or the horrors of withdrawal symptoms.

It is not only sufferers who need support and under-standing. Relatives also need someone to talk to.

Of course, one of the reasons people avoid joining a self-help group is that they have to admit openly that they need help. They have to admit they are vulnerable. Carers, particularly, feel terribly guilty at times when they feel that they just cannot cope any more, or even just do not want to. However joining any self-help group is not a sign of weakness. Just the opposite — it is a sign of great strength.

At the end of this chapter is a list of such self-help groups. It isn't comprehensive and there may not be a branch of a particular group in your area. If you want to know about local services, then you can check with your GP practice, library or local newspaper. By contacting the national office of the appropriate organisation they can let you know of local branches in your area.

Art therapy

Art therapy works on the basis that a person's fundamental thoughts and feelings, hidden in their subconscious, are more easily expressed through images than words. The art therapist allows a client to work with a medium they feel comfortable with, and observes how the client behaves, how materials are used, how the image is made, the content of the work, the dependence on the therapist and so on, and is able to work with these observations interpretively to help the client achieve greater self-awareness.

Therapy moves through four basic stages:

— building a relationship with the therapist and, perhaps, learning to play

— regression and abreaction of trauma

— testing of 'real' relationships, developing impulse control and self-esteem

— termination of the therapeutic relationship

Referral to an art therapist or art therapy group can be done in a number of ways depending on the organisation and client.

Availability of therapy

Gaining access to any form of therapy is easy if you have plenty of time (therapy usually means between one and three sessions a week for two or more years), and money. However, for most of us, regular therapy sessions would be something of a luxury, even with a strong belief in its value. Of course, psychotherapy is available on the NHS.

The main providers of psychotherapy through the NHS are mental health nurses, clinical psychologists, psychiatrists and quite often occupational therapists. Mental health nurses are increasing being trained as counsellors and may also take additional training in psychotherapy, group and individual analysis and behaviour therapy. Clinical psychologists, who are much fewer in number than mental health nurses, study counselling psychology as part of their training. Some psychiatrists train as therapists or analysts although many more do not. Occupational therapists are increasingly becoming involved in group work, while some take courses in counselling. These professionals deal with people experiencing a wide range of mental distress including anxiety, phobias, depression, sexual and marital problems, bereavement issues and so on.

Some community mental health nurses and psychology services work on a self-referral basis, ie you would phone the mental health service directly and ask to speak to a nurse or psychologist. Other services work by taking referrals from family doctors. If you are unsure how your local mental health service works then your GP is probably the best place to start. If he or she is unsympathetic then consult another GP.

The waiting time for an appointment with some of these mental health professionals can sometimes be several weeks, depending on the urgency of your case.

Organisations offering therapy

The Tavistock Clinic is an NHS institution that provides mainly short-term and some long-term psychotherapy based on a psychoanalytic approach. Because it is run by the NHS there is usually no charge for therapy. Sessions are usually once a week with a background in psychiatry, psychology, social work or mental health nursing.

The Arbours Association offers psychotherapy to people who experience mental distress even if this is sometimes of a psychotic nature. They try to keep their charges to a minimum in order to offer their service to people on limited incomes and charge between £8 to £15 and sometimes less depending on need and means.

The Association for Group and Individual Psychotherapy also uses an analytical approach. Fees vary from between £10 and £25.

The British Association of Psychotherapists is involved in the training of analytical psychotherapists but can also offer a clinical assessment and referral service (ie they will refer you to a person they feel can deal with your needs). Fees vary but are usually between £10 and £25 per session. A client may be involved in between one and three sessions a week.

The Camden Psychotherapy Unit is free to residents of Camden. The approach is one of psychoanalytical psychotherapy.

The majority of psychotherapy units seem to be based in London. However, there are local services. The British Association of Psychotherapists can provide a contact in your area.

It may be that you feel your problem is not serious enough to be dealt with by a mental health professional or you may feel that there is a certain stigma to using mental health services. In this case you may prefer to contact an organisation that offers counselling in a specific field.

The Samaritans is an organisation that does not just deal with people who are suicidal but also with people who need someone to talk their problems over with or with people who are very lonely. By befriending people, the Samaritans are able to help with very difficult life problems.

Relate (formerly Marriage Guidance Council) specialises in helping people with relationship difficulties, whether they are married or single. Both the Samaritans and Relate have local branches and advertise in local newspapers. Their telephone numbers can be found in local telephone directories.

CRUSE offers support and counselling for bereaved people and is another organisation with local branches.

Alcoholics Anonymous is an example of an organisation that tackles a life problem through the use of group therapy. Your local newspaper will give you a more comprehensive list of local services as will your local mental health service and GP.

If you decide that you would like to invest in some therapy and have an idea which type you would like to try, then magazines like Human Potential and MIND carry advertisements by private therapists. An advertisement, of course, is no guide to their ability. And nor are their prices. However, you may feel that you do not want an orthodox therapy service but are particularly interested in, say, a feminist or new-man approach or you may be from another culture and feel you need therapy that is in touch with your situation. In these cases it may be harder but not impossible to find an appropriate therapy centre. The Inter-Cultural Therapy Centre in London, the Birmingham Women's Counselling and Therapy Centre and the Women's Counselling and Therapy Service in Leeds are examples of therapy centres that focus on particular needs.

If you subscribe to a private health plan through BUPA or Private Patients' Plan you can usually claim for your psychotherapy sessions as long as these have been recommended by a doctor.

When it comes to choosing a therapist then with the best will in the world, the choice is bound to be a bit 'potluck'. Even if you rely on recommendation, the therapist that your best friend thinks the sun shines out of could turn out to be someone that you hate! The main things to ensure are that your therapist is:

—responsible
—reliable
—reasonably priced
—registered (for instance with the British Association of Psychotherapists)

As a final word on this subject it is only fair to point out that therapy is often, particularly in the early stages, both painful and difficult. The old adage 'no gain without pain' is certainly true. It should also be said that not everyone benefits from therapy nor is it a substitute for other human, loving relationships. However, therapy succeeds in as much as it can enable us to achieve these.

USEFUL ADDRESSES

Arbours Association 41a Weston Park, London N8. 081 340 7646.

Specialises in crisis work as well as short and long-term therapy. Fees vary often depending on income and need.

Association for Group and Individual Psychotherapy 29 St Mark's Crescent, London NW1. 071 485 9141.

Fees vary according to need and therapist.

Association of Jungian Analysts Flat 3, 7 Eton Avenue, London, NW3 3EL. 071 794 8711.

Covers mainly the south-east of England. No NHS treatment. Fees vary from less than £5 (trainee analyst) to around £30 (trained analyst).

Birmingham Women's Counselling and Therapy Centre 43 Ladywood,   Middleway, Birmingham, B16 8HA. 021 455 8677.

Feminist approach. Treatment is free.

British Association of Psychotherapists 121 Hendon Lane, London, N3 3PR. 081 346 1747.

Mainly involved in the training of analytical psycho-therapists but can also provide a clinical assessment and referral service. No NHS treatment.

British Association for Counselling 37a Sheep Street, Rugby, Warwickshire, CV21 3BX. 0788 78328/9.

A resource centre. Offers no direct service.

Camden Psychotherapy Unit 25–31 Tavistock Place, London, WC1H 9SE. 071 388 2071.

Free psychotherapy centre for Camden residents.

Carrs Lane Counselling Centre Carrs Lane Centre, Birmingham, B4 7SX. 021 643 6363.

No set fees although donations are welcome.

Institute of Psychotherapy and Social Studies 5 Lake House, London, NW3 2SH. 071 794 4147.

Psychotherapy with a psychodynamic and humanistic approach. No NHS treatment but reduced fee therapy available from trainees.

The Isis Centre 43 Little Clarendon Street, Oxford, OX1 2HU. 0865 56648.

All treatment on NHS. Clients must live in county of

Oxfordshire. Centre provides individual, marital and family counselling on a one-to-one and group basis.

Lincoln Clinic and Institute for Psychotherapy 77 Westminster Bridge Road, London, SE1 7HS. 071 928 7211.

This training centre offers analytical psychotherapy and also briefer therapy that focuses on life problems. No NHS treatment is available but fees can vary according to means.

London Centre for Psychotherapy 19 Fitzjohn's Avenue, London, NW3 5JY. 071 435 0873.

Therapy is analytical in nature and fees per session are around £10.

Nafsiyat The Inter-Cultural Therapy Centre, 278 Seven Sisters Road, London, N4 2HY. 071 263 4130.

This centre offers psychodynamic psychotherapy with a particular regard for cultural issues. Fees are around £15 although sessions are free to people in the Islington area.

Relate See your local telephone directory.

Scottish Institute of Human Relations 56 Albany Street, Edinburgh. 031 556 6454.

Takes a psychoanalytical approach to psychotherapy. No NHS treatment. Fees around £20 per session.

South London, Psychotherapy Group Teddington, Middlesex, TW11 9QT. 081 977 6303.

Takes a psychoanalytic approach to psychotherapy. No NHS treatment although would probably refer to NHS therapist if necessary. Fees up to £25 per session.

Tavistock Clinic Adult Department, 120 Belsize Lane, London, NW3 5BA. 071 435 7111.

This is an NHS unit and so no fees are charged.

Women's Counselling and Therapy Service Top Floor, Oxford Chambers, Oxford Place, Leeds, LS1 3AX. 0532 455725.

Feminist/humanistic approach. Fees charged from £3 to £15 but also some free places.

Women's Therapy Centre 6 Manor Gardens, London, N7 6LA. 071 263 6200.

This centre provides short and long-term therapy on an individual and group basis. Fees vary according to client's situation and income.

5
SURVIVING
COMMUNITY
CARE

Community care is the term used for the 'new wave' approach to mental health care provision. It refers to the closing down of large scale Victorian institutions with their miles of echoing corridors and sad, shuffling feet going nowhere. It is an acknowledgement of the stultifying effect on the human soul caused by incarceration in impersonal surroundings with impersonal care, that takes away rather than builds upon the living skills of people with long-term mental health problems.

Approximately one in seven people reading this book may need to have mental health care from a variety of sources, from their GP to their local mental health hospital. This chapter gives some information about the range of services that they provide.

When we talk of mental health care there is a tendency to think of psychiatrists, hospitals and not a great deal else. This way of thinking is firmly stuck in the so-called medical model, a service dominated by doctors dealing with illness. However, this approach to mental health care and service provision is now dying out, although perhaps not fast enough. In fact, many mental health services and providers of mental health care have nothing to do with hospitals or even the National Health Service.

Mental *health* depends on a great many things. For a woman who is isolated at home with young children, her mental health may depend upon friendly neighbours, a local playgroup, access to good transport and a supportive partner. For people who have had a long period in a psychiatric hospital, it can be the ability to cope with everyday things like shopping, cooking, making a telephone call or building a social life. After having had most of the decisions about these things taken away from them, developing life skills becomes essential to their mental health survival.

For a newly retired woman who has worked all her adult life, mental health survival may depend on her ability to make the transition from a life of work to a life of recreation. She may need to learn to structure her own time and to make new friends. To someone who experiences recurring bouts of depression, mental health survival may depend on building a good prevention strategy, ensuring a healthy, regular diet, sufficient exercise and positive thinking. For most of us financial security plays an important part in our mental health.

Whatever it takes to ensure our mental health, one thing is certain, we cannot do without help.

The people who are best at surviving life's 'little dilemmas' are the ones who are able to get help when they need it. They seem to be skilled at finding out what is available and not too proud to ask for help.

Asking for help when we need it is something that we seem to find very difficult to do. Hiding our feelings, coping by ourselves, not needing others; for some strange reason these seem to be extolled as virtues. But while it may not do to be crying on everyone's shoulder all the time, or to allow ourselves to be totally dependent on others and refuse to fend for ourselves, there seems to be some reluctance to pitch into the middle ground. There are people and organisations whose specific purpose is to help others, to provide a service that is very much needed — and there is some skill in finding and approaching these.

Help can come in a variety of ways. Support groups, telephone helplines, counselling services, social groups and the statutory services provided by the health and social services are around for people who need them and know how to get access to them.

FINDING SUPPORT

This book can only provide a very general guide to advice and support and, as has been said before, individual needs vary widely. For this reason it is important that you have a good idea what support services are available in your area. Your local Citizen's Advice Bureau is a good starting point as is your nearest large library. Ideally your local health authority and social services departments can be helpful, although it is sometimes difficult to get through to the right person and some local authorities are more helpful than others. Kent County Council Social Services Department, for instance, has had a local directory produced called *Positive Ways To Look After Your Mental Health* that includes a wide range of services that could be said to promote mental health.

ACCOMMODATION

Shelter is a basic need, and yet rather than ensure that everyone has access to some form of warm, secure shelter, this basic need is firmly in the grip of a market economy that means too many people live in inadequate housing or may even become homeless.

From a mental health perspective decent, reasonably priced accommodation is vital for the following reasons:

- It gives us warmth, shelter and security.
- It allows us to express ourselves.
- It is a place to bring friends.
- It allows us to share our lives in a family situation if we wish.
- It gives us a secure base from which to venture into perhaps less safe territory.
- It may give us a sense of pride and add to our self-esteem.
- It gives us an address — very important if we need to claim unemployment benefit.
- If we live alone, it can give us privacy although it might also isolate us from others and make us lonely.

- If we share our accommodation, it can give us companionship although it may detract from our need for privacy.

The nature and quality of our accommodation is therefore very important to our overall mental as well as physical well-being. Of course, there are people who choose not to tie themselves to accommodation because of the associated responsibilities of cost, conformity and company. However, these are perhaps a small proportion of the homeless, many of whom have had to leave homes or accommodation that provided few of them with the benefits listed above. For others it is often nothing more than the lack of availability of affordable housing; unfortunately, our capitalist economy means that our most basic needs are often the costliest to fulfill.

For people whose accommodation situation is a particular issue for them because their existing situation is detrimental to their mental health, there are some organisations that can help. Shelter, for instance, is a national organisation with local branches, the aim of which is to help people find accommodation. Local Housing Associations provide accommodation at reasonable rents and are a good alternative to local authority housing, although the demand for both is high.

Organisations such as the Elderly Accommodation Counsel Ltd and Age Concern can offer advice and guidance for elderly people needing more appropriate accommodation. If it is a care home that is needed, then the British Federation of Care Home Proprietors or the National Confederation of Registered Residential Care Homes Association are worth contacting.

Short-term shelter is provided by organisations such as the Salvation Army and the YMCA. Your local telephone directory should provide addresses and telephone numbers for your area.

Post-hospital accommodation People who have become homeless after a long period in a psychiatric hospital have very particular problems to overcome. Suitable housing should be arranged by the hospital with a social worker or perhaps a specially appointed accommodation officer. The choices are:

- lodgings with a family who let a room in their house;
- sheltered flats or bed-sitting rooms which are for those most able to live independent lives;
- hostels, some of which may provide support for residents with previous mental health problems and others which only provide basic bed and breakfast;
- group homes are usually schemes run by social services, voluntary organisations or health authorities. These vary in size and professional support is provided in line with the needs of the residents.

However, it may well be that 'official' housing is not something you are happy with or believe you need. If this is the case then you may wish to take control over your own housing situation. To an extent this means that you become vulnerable to the cut and thrust of market forces. If you go this route then ensure you have support from people who know their way around the housing arena. As well as consulting Shelter and the Housing Association, you can check your local Yellow Pages and Citizen's Advice Bureau for local housing schemes.

There are a number of national and regional organisations that offer accommodation for people who have been in hospital because of their mental health problems (addresses at end of chapter). These include:

- The Arbours Association, which has long-stay houses in London run on a therapeutic community basis.
- Guideposts which is a project based service that provides accommodation for ex-patients supported by a social worker, community mental health nurse as well as local volunteers.
- Mental After Care Association which covers south-east England. This provides half-way accommodation (ie a stepping stone to more permanent individual accom-

modation), residential care for people over 65 and for those who need greater support and some respite care to allow people who care for those with high dependency mental health problems, like Alzheimer's disease, to have a break.

- Psychiatric Rehabilitation Association providing accommodation in London on a group or more individual basis (known as 'cluster' flats). They also have an Intensive Care Accommodation section which is staffed for people who may be experiencing a mental health crisis but who do not need hospital care.
- Local MIND schemes which have advice and contacts that are invaluable to people experiencing accommodation difficulties. There is a housing team based at the national MIND headquarters in London (see address at end of chapter).
- The St Mungo Housing Scheme which exists to improve the quality of life for single homeless people by providing accommodation and support services to help them progress towards greater self-sufficiency and, where possible, independence in the community. This community housing scheme is based in London.
- The Life Care and Housing Trust which provides accommodation and support for unsupported pregnant women and women with babies. Advice and other practical help is also available.
- The Richmond Fellowship offers residential accommodation run on a therapeutic community basis. Some of the homes are set up for people who are experiencing particular mental health problems such as those caused by schizophrenia or drug dependency.

For information on schemes in your area, check your local Yellow Pages under Housing Associations, Societies and Trusts, your local Citizen's Advice Bureau or your Local Authority Housing Department.

Homes for the elderly Perhaps one of the most difficult times many elderly people have to face is when they have to admit that they are no longer able to live completely independent, that they will have to rely on others. This is difficult not only because of pride and fear of encroaching dependence, but also because, as they start to lose control over their own situation, they have to rely on others and the care they provide. And good and bad residential care exists in both the private and public sectors.

Your local Citizen's Advice Bureau and social services department will provide you with a list of local residential homes. Those which belong to the National Confederation of Registered Residential Care Home Associations or the British Federation of Care Home Proprietors (see addresses below) should follow guidelines issued by these organisations which offer more than that recommended by the government, including activities programmes.

EMPLOYMENT

Due to the nature of mental health problems, the disruptive effect they can have on someone's life and the outdated attitudes of many employers it is difficult for some people, particularly those who have repeated experiences of mental distress, to maintain full-time employment.

For some it is possible to find work on an assisted scheme such as Remploy, the Psychiatric Rehabilitation Association, some local branches of MIND and the Richmond Fellowship. However, many people want to return to full-time employment and do not wish to experience prejudice as a result of their illness. Firms employing more than 20 people are by law required to reserve 3 per cent of their posts for people registered as disabled. Whether or not an individual would see his or her problem as 'disabling' is debatable. A discussion with the Disablement Resettlement Officer at the local Job Centre might provide some guidance and support.

The St Mungo Hostel and Care Services offer hands-on skills training, employment counselling and work experience placements which help to improve employment prospects with local employers.

It should be stressed here that a mental health problem on its own is not grounds for dismissal, although poor work performance or absenteeism for long periods of time are.

For those unable to work in the short or long term, financial advice is available from your local NHS mental health centre (social worker or MIND branch).

GETTING TO KNOW PEOPLE

Mental distress of any form often makes forming relationships that bit more difficult, and heaven knows, it isn't easy for any of us. Other people can sometimes make us want to withdraw. The sheer effort of 'being social' can wear us out. But at the same time, the need for other people remains.

In order to get support on a more casual basis than from a mental health professional or practical organisation, it is necessary to build a support network. And that means getting to know people. Most social situations (ironically) are designed for people who already know people. They are not designed for people who are on their own.

Many social settings can in fact feel quite threatening. In order to make the first tentative steps towards building up new relationships it is important to make a few small, successful steps to build up confidence.

Local mental health organisations, such as MIND, arrange coffee mornings and other meetings, such as stress management and relaxation groups. These offer the chance to meet other people, learn or practise useful health-promoting skills in an environment where you may be able to share your experiences with others who understand. If you feel you would like support from people who can associate with your experience of mental distress then you may wish to join a group such as the Schizophrenia Fellowship.

Alternatively you may feel you do not want to gain support from an organisation directly associated with mental health, in which case another option, depending on your age, sex or situation, might be more appropriate. Your local newspaper/'phone directory should have organisations such as Gingerbread (for single parents); Compassionate Friends (for bereaved parents); Association of Carers (for people looking after dependent relatives); Red Cross; CRUSE (for bereaved families) listed.

Voluntary organisations allow you to work as many hours as you feel able, to give something to others and to meet people at the same time. Although this is no substitute for paid employment if that is what you want and feel able to pursue, voluntary work does give a great deal. Voluntary organisations are often listed in local newspapers or can be found under the heading 'Charitable and Benevolent Organisations' in the Yellow Pages. Some towns have a voluntary work co-ordinating office and your Citizen's Advice Bureau or local social services department should know if this is the case. As well as the better known organisations, such as the Red Cross, Oxfam and Age Concern, there are local organisations set up to help local people, as well as national campaigning organisations, like the Friends of the Earth and Greenpeace.

If you are single and feel you would like to start a relationship, then there are groups set up to allow divorced, separated and single people to meet and socialise. These are sometimes run by religious organisations, but might also be set up and run by enthusiastic individuals who are fed up with a social scene dominated by couples.

If you are able to afford it, evening and day classes are available at local colleges. As well as meeting other people, these classes can help you gain new skills or qualifications. Reduced rates are usually available for people on limited incomes.

HEALTH CARE SERVICES

Acute hospital care
Going into hospital can be a frightening experience for

anyone, but because of the stigma that is still unfortunately attached to a psychiatric hospital, the event can be an extremely distressing one that may well aggravate the mental distress the person may have been admitted with in the first place. Much of this fear and stigma is attached to the old style asylums, still referred to as lunatic asylums during the early part of this century. It is no wonder that someone who is suffering from post-natal depression or who is finding it difficult to come to terms with a bereavement, who may be suffering from very frightening hallucinations or the withdrawal symptoms of alcohol or drug addiction becomes increasingly distressed at the thought of being called 'mad'.

Not all people suffering from mental health problems have insight into their need for hospital care, and in these instances it is necessary to implement the provisions of the Mental Health Act 1983, which lays down clear guidelines as to what rights the mental health staff have to assess and treat a patient, and what rights the patient has. However, while the Mental Health Act has an important part to play in the care of mental distress its use can be very distressing, as the patient often feels criminalised. This subject is covered more fully in Chapter 6.

For many people who need intensive support, close observation and careful assessment the environment of a hospital is very important. For most people the stay will be approximately six weeks. Staff are careful that a patient is not discharged prematurely thereby putting them at risk of a relapse.

With the continued closure of the old-type asylums, people are increasingly likely to be admitted to a ward in a district general hospital that specialises in mental health problems, in the same way as other wards specialise in maternity services or surgical after-care. While in hospital, the patient may well be offered therapies including occupational therapy (see p. 127), group therapy, counselling (on a one-to-one basis), recreational excursions (for those who are well enough), as well as the chance to develop many of their practical and coping skills. Some hospitals offer a separate rehabilitation service which is designed to reintroduce people to the community after a long hospital stay.

People needing long-term support are given this, wherever possible, in the community. If the patient does not have their own home or a family, then they may be placed in a group home, hostel or lodgings depending on their needs (see Accommodation above). There can be little argument, however, that community housing schemes are still too far and few between.

Day hospitals

A day hospital offers a range of services that help people experiencing mental health problems but who do not need in-patient care. Patients may be involved in occupational or art therapy, group therapy, and counselling, as well as having the opportunity to socialise with other people. It is probably fair to say that in a day hospital the emphasis is on skills development.

Day hospitals are ideal for people needing 'depot' injections — weekly, fortnightly or monthly injections of a tranquilliser to help contain unwanted symptoms such as experienced in schizophrenic type illnesses — these may be administered at the day hospital.

They are usually open around 10 o'clock in the morning to 4 o'clock in the afternoon.

Mental health centres

These tend to vary depending on the degree of progressiveness of the managers and health professionals involved. They can include a drop-in centre, a GP, community mental health nurses, psychologists, social workers and voluntary workers. Quite often these centres are centres for professionals rather than centres for patients. However, as more services look to consulting the users this may change.

MENTAL HEALTH CARE PROFESSIONALS

In the more progressive mental health services, the whole

emphasis of care is on helping the patient return to the community. Patients are encouraged through a programme of care operated by a team of professionals that will include several or all of the following: a mental health nurse, psychiatrist, psychologist, occupational therapist and social worker.

These professionals together make up what is known as a multidisciplinary team. It is usual that the psychiatrist is the team leader, although all team members are equally important to successful patient care.

Many teams allocate a key worker to each patient. The key worker has a special relationship with the patient and also ensures that the rest of the mental health team is aware of that patient's needs. The key worker is usually a mental health nurse or social worker, but can be an occupational therapist. In the community the key worker may be whoever has the closest contact with the patient. In some cases this might be someone like the home help.

In health authorities where primary nursing has been introduced the patient's main point of contact will be a mental health nurse (see below).

GP (general practitioner)

Although the GP is not traditionally seen as a mental health care professional and would not usually attend ward rounds as part of the multi-disciplinary team, he or she provides a great deal of mental health care, either in short-term prescribing of anti-depressants or anti-anxiolytics or just listening to people's emotional problems. It is usually the GP who will refer people on to specialists, such as the community mental health nurse, the clinical psychologist or the psychiatrist.

Mental health (psychiatric) nurse

The mental health nurse is the person with whom patients will have the most contact and who will probably be most important to their care. It is these specialist nurses who provide 24-hour care, and who monitor and assess an individual's progress. As part of the multi-disciplinary team they will discuss and agree a plan of care and in almost all cases this plan of care should be done in consultation with the patient. Although only the psychiatrist and his house officers (junior doctors) have the power to prescribe, the nurse's influence in deciding what to prescribe and in what dosage is very potent.

The modern mental health nurse is a highly skilled practitioner in the field of human activity, with an emphasis on self-awareness, interpersonal and organisational skills. They draw upon social and applied sciences including psychology, sociology, physiology and anatomy, medicine, pharmacology and psychiatry. They may specialise in care areas, such as the elderly, rehabilitation, child psychiatry or substance abuse.

Community mental health nurses visit people on an outpatient basis and provide a range of therapeutic services.

Psychiatrist

The psychiatrist is a qualified medical doctor who has gone on to specialise in psychiatry, and usually has consultant status. Patients have little contact with the consultant psychiatrist. Because he or she often appears to have a great deal of power and has certain legal and professional powers that a nurse does not have, patients tend to place a great deal of faith in this person and are sometimes disappointed. A survey conducted by MIND showed that nurses were the most helpful mental health professionals.

While there are many psychiatrists who are sensitive and empathic in the care they provide, many more are neither of these things and see their role as being that of a prescriber of pills.

Some psychiatrists are also trained psychotherapists, understanding the value of a planned programme of care that does not necessarily revolve around medication.

Clinical psychologist

A clinical psychologist specialises in the assessment and psychological care of mental health problems. Psychological testing, such as for IQ levels or for evidence of deep-seated mental health problems, is one area in which a clinical psychologist might work. They are also very involved in various therapies, such as counselling, family and behavioural therapy.

Mental health social worker

Some social workers choose to specialise in support of the family of people with mental health problems as well as the social aspects of care of the individual involved.

Such social workers can be based in a local mental health centre, mental health hospital or local authority offices. They can provide support and counselling as well as practical advice about welfare rights, local facilities and other day-to-day matters.

Occupational therapist

An occupational therapist is trained in various methods of helping people maintain and develop many of their social skills. As well as running occupational therapy workshops, including carpentry, pottery and craftwork, OT's get involved in reminiscence and group therapy.

Art therapist

Art therapy works from the basis that a person's fundamental thoughts and feelings, hidden in their subconscious, are more easily expressed through images than words. The art therapist allows a client to work with a medium they feel comfortable with, and observes how the client behaves, how materials are used, how the image is made, the content of the work, the dependence on the therapist and so on, and is able to work with these observations interpretively to help the client achieve greater self-awareness.

Art therapy is sometimes run as part of occupational therapy or may exist as a discipline in its own right.

Industrial therapist

Industrial therapy is designed to help people develop skills and confidence through a working environment. However, while it gives structure to the day and some of the benefits of a working environment, the work is often dull, repetitive and does not earn the patient more than pin money.

USEFUL ADDRESSES

Age Concern (England) Bernard Sunley House, 60 Pitcairn Road, Mitcham, Surrey CR4 3LL.

(Separate addresses for Scotland, Wales and Northern Ireland. Contact above for more information)

Arbours Association 41a Weston Park, London, N8 7BU. 081 340 7646.

Association of Carers 58 New Road, Chatham, Kent ME4 4OR. 0634 813981/2.

British Federation of Care Home Proprietors 51 Leopold Road, Felixstowe, Suffolk IP11 7NR. 0394 279539.

Citizen's Advice Bureau (see your local telephone directory).

CRUSE Cruse House, 126 Sheen Road, Richmond, Surrey TW9 1UR. 081 940 4818.

Elderly Accommodation Counsel Ltd 1 Durward House, 31 Kensington Court, London, W8 5BH. 071 937 8709.

Guideposts 2 Church Green, Witney, Oxon OX8 6AW. 0993 72886.

Kent County Council Social Services Department Fort Pitt House, New Road, Rochester ME1 1DU. 0634 815754.

Mental After Care Association Eagle House, 110 Jermyn Street, London, SW1Y 6HB.

MIND 22 Harley Street, London, W1N 2ED. 071 637 0741.

(See local directories or contact national office for local branches).

National Confederation of Registered Residential Care Homes Associations, 8 Southampton Place, London, WC1A 2EF. 071 405 2277.

Psychiatric After Care Association 21a Kingsland High Street, London, E8 2JS. 071 254 9753.

Richmond Fellowship 8 Addison Road, London, W14 8DL. 071 603 6373.

Samaritans 3 Hornton Place, London, W8. 071 283 3400.

St Mungo Housing Scheme 217 Harrow Road, London, W2 5XQ. 071 286 1358.

Shelter 88 Old Street, London, EC1V 9HU. 071 253 0202.

6.
MENTAL HEALTH AND HUMAN RIGHTS

Understanding and defending human rights, for ourselves and other people, has been a theme that has dominated the thinking of the twentieth century western world. But while there is now perhaps little question about the importance of human rights, there is a greater moral struggle when it comes to deciding the balance between the rights of the individual and the rights of the community; between the rights of the community and the rights of the state; and between the rights of individuals, communities and states.

While much of this book has talked about individual mental well-being from a positive point of view, for some people the lack of their mental well-being may well be caused by severe restrictions of many of their human rights, while for others it can mean that many of their rights are taken away from them. The right to freedom, the right to vote, the right to refuse medication, the right to wear their own clothes — all of these rights can be legally taken from an individual whose mental health state appears to create a risk of them harming themselves or others.

For this reason it is important to understand just what our rights are as individuals, under what circumstances we may have to surrender these rights and perhaps more crucially, what we can do to protect our rights and the rights of others.

THE PATIENTS' CHARTER

The Patients' Charter drawn up by the Association of Community Health Councils for England and Wales is a set of guidelines that includes both legal and human rights in relation to health care. These state that all persons have a right to:

- health services, appropriate to their needs, regardless of financial means or where they live, and without delay. This includes the right to change your hospital doctor if you are unhappy with any aspect of the care you are receiving;
- be treated with reasonable skill, care and consideration. According to the General Medical Council 'the public are entitled to expect that a registered medical practitioner will afford and maintain a good standard of medical care. This includes conscientious assessment of the history, symptoms and signs of a patient's condition; sufficiently thorough professional attention, examination and, where necessary, diagnostic investigation; competent and considerate professional management; appropriate and prompt action upon evidence suggesting existence of a condition requiring urgent medical intervention; and readiness, where the circumstances warrant it, to consult appropriate professional colleagues;
- written information about health services, including hospitals, community and general practitioner services;
- register with a GP with ease and to be able to change without adverse consequences;
- be informed about all aspects of their condition and proposed care (including the alternatives available), unless they express a wish to the contrary;
- accept or refuse treatment (including diagnostic procedures) without affecting the standard of alternative care given (under the Mental Health Act 1983 this right has certain restrictions which are outlined below);

- a second opinion;
- the support of a relative or friend at any time;
- advocacy (see below) and interpreting services;
- choose whether to participate or not in research trials and be free to withdraw at any time without affecting the standard of alternative care given;
- only be discharged from hospital after adequate arrangements have been made for their continuing care;
- privacy for all consultations;
- be treated at all times with respect for their dignity, personal needs and religious and philosophic beliefs;
- confidentiality of all records relating to their care;
- have access to their own health care records (still not a legal right);
- make a complaint and have it investigated thoroughly, speedily and impartially and be informed of the result;
- an independent investigation into all serious medical or other mishaps whilst in NHS care, whether or not a complaint is made and, where appropriate, adequate redress.

MENTAL HEALTH ACT 1983

Many of our rights are enshrined in law, and the legislation that covers our rights in relation to our mental health is called the Mental Health Act 1983. This Act was brought into being in order to protect individuals and the community in the event of severe mental distress that could in some way prove detrimental or dangerous to the individual suffering the distress or the public at large.

Safeguards are built into the Act to prevent abuse. Second opinions, tribunals and time limits have all been included in a legal attempt to protect people who may be very vulnerable and to prevent people being locked away and forgotten.

The Mental Health Act 1983 is very complicated and lengthy, and consequently cannot be dealt with comprehensively in this chapter. However, an attempt to inform people of some of their basic legal rights is included. But this chapter is not just about legal rights, important as these are. It is about human rights; the right to be listened to, not just at a tribunal but on a day-to-day basis; the right to be involved in the planning of care and treatment; the right to be involved in the development of mental health services; the right to privacy and to be treated with dignity regardless of mental state.

Along with the Mental Health Act are other movements that are striving to improve conditions and empower people who receive care via the mental health services. These include: the consumer movement (consumerism); patient advocacy; self-advocacy; and support groups.

Legal rights under the Mental Health Act 1983

There are still old black and white films around that follow the theme of the evil relative trying to get some poor soul committed to a lunatic asylum, usually as part of a plot to get the family wealth or perhaps run off with a lover. Although in practice this was probably a bit extreme, there were without doubt many instances where people who felt unable or unwilling to cope with a relative's mental distress did ask for the relative in question to be committed under the Mental Health Act.

Since 1983 and the revision of the Act it is now far more difficult to 'Section' a person. That is, there are safeguards built in to the law to prevent any one person having any one other person locked up in an institution forever.

Although the old movies might be good for a giggle, the realities of the Mental Health Act have serious consequences, of which it is important to be aware. For instance, if you decide that you need the help of mental health professionals and you decide, voluntarily, to enter a mental health hospital for a period of assessment and possible treatment, then you may well think you have exactly the same rights and considerations as someone entering a general hospital for an operation. However, this is not the case. If, after a period of voluntary stay in a mental health hospital, you decide you no longer need help and wish to discharge yourself, and the professionals concerned believe that you are at risk of, say, harming yourself or others, or are not well enough to leave, then they may well decide to keep you in hospital under a section of the Mental Health Act.

They can do this in a number of ways. For instance, in cases where an 'informal' patient (ie someone in hospital on a voluntary basis) wishes to leave the ward and he or she is felt to be at risk of harming themselves or some other person, then mental health nurses have the legal right to detain a patient for up to 6 hours (Section 5.4 — nurse's holding power). This holding power ceases the minute a doctor steps onto the ward. The doctor may or may not decide to implement a further Section of the Act. However, if a doctor cannot be found (and this should be a rare occurrence), there appears to be nothing within the 1983 Act to prevent a nurse implementing a second or even a third Section 5.4, thereby in practice preventing a patient from leaving the ward for some considerable period of time.

It is not only patients who have been held on a ward under this Section of the 1983 Mental Health Act. In one particular instance, a relative became hostile and abusive whilst visiting a patient on a psychiatric ward, with the result that the nurse in charge exercised her powers under the 1983 Mental Health Act and held him on the ward under Section 5.4 of the Act. This in fact was an abuse of the nurse's holding power, as she should have called the police.

Admission to and discharge from a hospital for people with acute or chronic mental health problems

Informal or Voluntary Admission (Section 131) Any person who requires treatment for mental disorder may request informal admission, but must be referred by a doctor. In the case of a person under 16 (a minor), this must be on the authority of his parent or guardian. An informal patient is free to leave hospital at any time subject to holding powers or common law powers. In nearly every respect, the legal position of an informal patient is the same as a patient in a general hospital.

Compulsory admission from patient's home
(Sections 2, 3 and 4)

Section 2 — Admission for assessment The criteria for admission are:

* mental disorder which warrants detention in hospital for assessment (treatment may be given);
* detention is necessary for patient's health or safety or for the protection of others.

An application for detention under Section 2 of the Mental Health Act (1983) can be made by the individual's nearest relative or an approved social worker. A medical recommendation that the person is detained under this section of the Act must be made by: 1) a doctor who knows the patient and 2) an approved medical officer.

The shorter Sections of the Mental Health Act (1983) that hold a patient in hospital for up to 72 hours cannot be appealed against, for the reason that by the time an appeal is set in motion the Section will have expired in any case. However Section 2 can be appealed against, but any such appeal must be made within 14 days of admission.

Section 2 terminates automatically after 28 days. It can be terminated by the responsible medical officer, by the managers of the hospital, or by the nearest relative (but only with the agreement of the responsible medical officer; if this agreement is not forthcoming, then your appeal should be lodged in writing to the hospital managers who can overrule the consultant).

It can also be terminated by a Mental Health Review Tribunal (see below for an explanation of this body). Lastly it can be terminated by the patient leaving hospital without permission (referred to as 'absent without leave') until the Section has expired.

Section 3 — Admission for treatment   To be brought into hospital under Section 3 of the Mental Health Act (1983) a person has to be suffering from one of four legal classifications of mental disorder:

- mental illness
- severe mental impairment
- mental impairment
- psychopathic disorder

In the case of psychopathic disorder or mental impairment, treatment must be likely to alleviate or prevent deterioration in the patient's condition (in many instances psychopathic/sociopathic disorders do not respond to treatment).

In instances where the possibility exists that a person may be a danger to themselves or others, they can be detained under Section 3 of the Mental Health Act.

As with Section 2, application to have someone brought into hospital under Section 3 can be made by the nearest relative or an approved social worker. However, the social worker cannot make the application without the consent of the nearest relative. Again, like Section 2, medical recommendation must be sought from a doctor who knows the patient plus one other approved medical officer.

A person can be kept in hospital for 6 months under Section 3 of the Mental Health Act, and this can be renewed for a further 6 months after this, followed by periods of one year. Section 3 can be terminated by the responsible medical officer, the hospital managers, the nearest relative (again, like Section 2, a request for termination can be overruled by the responsible medical officer) and the Mental Health Review Tribunal.

If a person goes absent without leave for 28 days (Section 18 (4)) or for 6 months (Section 17 (5)), the Section automatically becomes terminated.

Section 4 — Admission for assessment in an emergency
The criteria for admission under Section 4 of the Mental Health Act (1983) is the same as that for Section 2 when admission is of urgent necessity. Application can be made by the nearest relative or approved social worker, the difference being that Section 4 needs only the recommendation of the doctor who knows the patient.

Section 4 will expire after 72 hours unless a second medical recommendation is received. It can be terminated by the responsible medical officer or by the hospital managers or if the patient goes absent without leave until the Section expires.

It is important that people entering hospital as informal or voluntary patients are aware that if they wish to leave and their leaving is believed to be inadvisable by medical or nursing staff, then they can be legally detained.

A doctor can hold a patient in hospital, pending an application for compulsory detention, for 72 hours. This can be terminated by the responsible medical officer or hospital managers.

It is also possible for a patient to be detained in hospital for a maximum of 6 hours by nursing staff, if they believe that prevention from leaving hospital is necessary for the protection of the patient or others and it is not possible to gain the immediate attendance of the responsible medical officer or nominated substitute.

Consent to treatment
The Mental Health Act contains the legal situation with regard to a patients' right to refuse treatment. It applies to any patient detained under the Act, except those detained under Section 4 (see above). Section 5, Section 35 (remand to hospital for reports on accused's mental condition), patients conditionally discharged under Sections 42, 73 or 74 who have not been brought back into hospital, as well as Section 135 (warrant to search for and remove patients) and Section 136 (mentally disordered person found in public places).

Surgical operations that interfere with the workings of

the brain (eg lobotomy) are dealt with under Section 57 of the Act. In this instance it is necessary for the patient themselves to give consent and for a registered medical practitioner plus two other people who are not registered medical practitioners to state in writing that the person to undergo the operation is capable of understanding the nature, purpose and likely effects of the operation and that they have given their consent.

However, very few people coming into contact with the mental health services will have any dealings with Section 57, as operations to remove parts of the brain are rare, and it is more likely to be in the area of refusing medication or electro-convulsive therapy (ECT) that the patients' rights might be dismissed.

Refusing medication: the informal patient   It is a sad fact that many doctors and nurses working within the mental health field do not listen to what patients have to say about their medication. Indeed all too often any concerns raised by the patient about medication are regarded as 'inappropriate behaviour' and refusal to take medication is regarded as 'non-compliance'. Non-compliance in turn can have unpleasant consequences for the patient, including evidence for detaining an informal patient and in the case of the detained patient it may result in evidence against the termination of a section and quite possibly medication given by injection (most medication is given orally) against the patient's wishes.

As the law stands at present, an informal patient in a mental health hospital has the same rights as a patient in hospital with a physical illness:

- The implications of the treatment or procedure should be explained (in the case of psychotropic drugs or ECT, this should include an explanation about side effects).
- The patient retains the right to refuse the treatment offered.

Treatment given without consent is regarded as battery, a form of trespass to the person, and this can lead to legal action in the criminal and civil courts.

In the case of what is seen as 'urgent necessity', a doctor might decide, following consultation with colleagues, to give treatment where informed consent is uncertain and the patient is at risk. This authority is derived from common law.

A relative's consent has no validity under the law.

Refusing medication: the detained patient The nature of some mental health problems can mean that the sufferer is not aware of the nature and extent of what they are experiencing and the possible consequences to themselves and others. For instance, a person who is experiencing an extreme manic episode may well not eat or sleep for days, and could be in danger of putting such a strain on their physical system that they may collapse and die from exhaustion. However, because they are so elated in mood, they may well respond to the offer of treatment by saying that they have never felt so well in their lives.

Their insight may well be impaired, perhaps partially, perhaps totally. In such instances it may be necessary to give treatment to get the person to a state whereby they can discuss their care with nursing staff or their doctor. Where medication has to be given without consent, specific statutory authority may be required.

However, again, there are certain issues that patients need to be aware of with regard to their right to refuse both ECT and medication:

CONSENT TO TREATMENT — BASIC PRINCIPLES

- The patient's informed consent is required before certain designated treatments can be administered to patients detained under a section which authorises treatment.
- If the patient is unable to give informed consent in relation to these treatments or irrationally refuses consent, treatment may be given only if the opinion of a second independent psychiatrist is in agreement and

after he has consulted other non-medical members of the clinical team who know the patient.

- Some specified treatments 'of special concern' may be given only with the patient's informed consent, the endorsement of the validity of that consent by an independent panel, together with the clinical approval of an independent psychiatrist after he has consulted other members of the clinical team. These opinions are required when the specified treatments are to be given to detained or informal patients. For this group the consent of the patient is an absolute requirement.

- Medication (not included in the arrangements outlined in the previous paragraphs) may be given without the patient's consent and without the need to obtain a second opinion for up to three months. After this period of time, consent or the endorsement of an independent psychiatrist is necessary to continue. Long-term administration requires a periodic report at the time of renewal of the detention order.

- A second opinion may be given for a treatment plan involving several treatments given over a period of time.

- The patient may withdraw consent. Continuation of treatment without the consent of the patient would then require the approval of an independent psychiatrist.

- Urgent treatment involving the use of treatments controlled in other circumstances may be given to patients detained for treatment without consent, or a second opinion for defined purposes.

- Urgent treatment for physical illness (not mentioned in the Act) may be given with the authority of the common law, but non-urgent treatment for physical illness would normally require the patient's consent. The criteria facing the doctor are those applicable to an informal psychiatric patient and any patient under medical or surgical care.

- Any treatment which has not been specified as one which requires any of the procedures described above may be given to a detained patient (for instance, nursing care, occupational therapy, rehabilitation).

- The Secretary of State, with advice, will list the treatments to be included in each category in Regulations and may change the category from time to time.
- Independent second medical opinions will be given by psychiatric members of the Mental Health Act Commissioners or doctors appointed by the Commission to perform this task on behalf of the Secretary of State (obtained by telephoning the relevant Commission Office — see Useful Addresses below).

(From *A Guide To The Mental Health Act 1983* by Robert Bluglass, Churchill Livingstone, 1984.)

However, although the legislators have done their best to build in safeguards for the patient by bringing in second opinions, it can do nothing to prevent clinicians persuading these so-called independent opinions to see their point of view and this persuasion happens. I witnessed an occupational therapist support the decision to give ECT to a patient who was unable to give consent, despite the fact that the occupational therapist admitted that she did not really know the patient and had indeed only seen her in passing on a couple of occasions. And despite the fact that the occupational therapist made her reluctance known, she was persuaded to support the proposed treatment.

Sections 128 and 134

The Mental Health Act protects patients' rights in a number of ways. Under Section 128 of the Mental Health Act, for instance, it is an offence for a male employee of a hospital or mental health nursing home to have sexual intercourse with a female patient or commit homosexual acts with a male patient suffering from mental distress and residing at the establishment at which he works.

Section 134 covers rights regarding patient's mail. There can be no restrictions placed on the mail of an informal patient. For a detained patient, no mail may be stopped going to or coming from the following: any health authority including the Mental Health Act Commission; the Court of Protection; the European Commission on Human Rights; government ministers or Members of Parliament; hospital managers; or the patient's legal representatives.

MENTAL HEALTH REVIEW TRIBUNALS

Mental Health Review Tribunals are independent bodies set up under the Mental Health Act to enable patients to appeal against their detention or to have this automatically reviewed.

The members of the Tribunal are appointed by the Lord Chancellor (the highest legal person in the land) and consist of lay (not a professional connected with the mental health field) people, doctors, legal members (circuit judges or lawyers of equal rank and experience).

Hearings are usually held at the hospital in which the patient is being detained. These can be open or closed, formal or informal, depending on the situation. Details of the circumstances under which a patient can appeal to a Tribunal are included with the relevant section above.

THE MENTAL HEALTH CONSUMER MOVEMENT

Traditionally, receivers or purchasers of goods and services have been fairly powerless and often vulnerable to unscrupulous providers and profiteers. The need to protect consumers and also to instil a stronger sense of morality and responsibility in providers resulted in the growth of the consumer movement. Listening to the customer became a watchword for successful organisations, and market research the communication link between goods and service providers and their customers.

This movement was initially slow to catch on in the UK, but during the 1980s under a confident Tory government, consumerism has encompassed not only commerce and industry but the public health care sector as well.

The NHS, during the greater part of the 1980s, was the focus of attention for customer satisfaction surveys.

Usually instigated by senior management, these surveys were developed and carried out as a way of improving the quality of care that patients received. Concentrating mainly on the so-called hotel services (quality of food, comfort, pleasantness of environment), it neatly skirted issues of relevance to user empowerment, such as involvement in treatment and access to medical records, and rarely looked to users of mental health services, preferring to tap into the feelings of satisfaction or otherwise experienced by people using the acute general services (eg maternity, medical and surgical wards).

As a form of promoting mental health rights, consumerism does not show any great promise except perhaps where it stimulates mental health workers to see patients as partners in a giving and receiving relationship (the giving and receiving goes both ways, not just from professional to patient).

Patients' Councils

The first patients' council was established in Nottingham. A patients' council is a meeting of hospital residents or patients without the presence of staff (which differs from community meetings where staff and patients meet together). The meeting does not need a statutory number of patients to attend and attendance is from choice. Any issue of importance to patients can be discussed and decisions made about how to improve the quality of environment, care received or anything else of importance to the patients themselves.

In Nottingham the patients' councils from individual wards elected representatives (always a patient) to meet with other patient representatives of other wards at a Hospital Council to discuss matters that affected all wards in order to take these issues to hospital management.

The role of advocacy in achieving mental health rights

The term 'advocacy' means the pleading of a case on behalf of another. The main kinds of advocacy that exist

143

in the mental health field are: patient advocacy (see patients councils); paid advocacy (the legal represent-ation); self-advocacy.

Self-advocacy Speaking up for ourselves is all too rarely encouraged, particularly if what we have to say goes against the grain. And so in many areas of our lives we tend to allow or even pay for others to speak on our behalf: lawyers, trade union representatives and politicians are just a few of the people who may represent our views and feelings on a variety of issues. However, the problems with representatives is that quite often they may think they know how we feel and what we want, but in actual fact they may be quite out of touch. They may not consult fully enough with us or they may think they know better. For this reason it is often important that we do speak up for ourselves. To do this effectively we need knowledge, skill and support. And perhaps courage.

For people who have used mental health services, speak-ing up for themselves is far from easy. They are told, and often accept, that doctors and nurses know best. They are pushed into a passive, accepting role, and any attempt to reject this role is often seen as a symptom of a psychiatric illness rather than a welcome sign of well-being. Given the amount of social stigma that is attached to mental health problems of most kinds it is a very brave person who stands up and admits their situation, let alone fights for their needs. It is, for many people, far less painful to put their experience behind them and to get on with their lives.

However, despite the very real difficulties and risk of self-advocacy, there are those who do wish to make their views known and implement change and they draw strength from linking up with like-minded others. Sur-vivors Speak Out (see Useful Addresses below) is a national mental health service users self-advocacy network that facilitates:

- communication between individuals and groups involved in self-advocacy;

- consciousness-raising for survivors and mental health workers;
- information for mental health workers about the value of self-advocacy and opportunities for them to give their personal and financial support.

This network does not represent users of mental health services, but works to help them represent themselves, and to encourage service providers to listen and promulgate self-advocacy amongst patients.

USEFUL ADDRESSES

Association of Community Health Councils for England and Wales, 362 Euston Road, London W1M 4AT. 071 388 4814.

ASYLUM (A Journal for Democratic Psychiatry), Department of Psychiatry, Royal Hallamshire Hospital, Sheffield.

British Medical Association, BMA House, Tavistock Square, London WC1N 9JP. 071 387 4499.

British Network for Alternatives to Psychiatry, 158 Rivermead Court, Hurlingham, London NW6.

Camden Mental Health Consortium, c/o Frank Bangay, 28a Edgar House, Kingsmead Estate, Homerton Road, London E9.

Commission for Complaints, (Northern Ireland), Progressive House, 33 Wellington Place, Belfast, BT1 6HN. 0232 233821.

Consumers' Association, 2 Marylebone Road, London, NW1 4DX. 071 486 5544.

Contact, Chesterfield Community Centre, Tontine Road, Chesterfield.

Good Practices in Mental Health, 380–384 Harrow Road, London W9. 071 289 2034.

Interdisciplinary Association of Mental Health Workers, Department of Educational Studies, University of Surrey, Guildford.

Lambeth Link-Self-Advocacy Project, 30a Acre Lane, London SW2 5SG.

National Association for Patient Participation, Hazelbank, Peaselake, Guildford, Surrey, GU5 9RJ.

Nottingham Advocacy Group, 65 Birkin Avenue, Hyson Green, Nottingham.

Nottingham Patients' Council, Support Group, 114 Mansfield Road, Nottingham.

Survivors Speak Out, 33 Lichfield Road, London NW2.

Mental Health Review Tribunals — regional offices

Mental Health Review Tribunals, Rm 1407, Euston Tower, 286 Euston Road, London NW1 3DN. 071 388 1188.

Mental Health Review Tribunals, 3rd Floor, Cressington House, 249 St Mary's Road, Garston, Liverpool, L19 0NF. 051 494 0095.

Mental Health Review Tribunals, Spur A, Block 5, Government Buildings, Chalfont Drive, Western Boulevard, Nottingham NG8 3RZ. 0602 294222/3.

Mental Health Review Tribunals, 2nd Floor, New Crown Buildings, Cathays Park, Cardiff CF1 3NQ. 0222 825798.

Mental Health Act Commission — Regional Offices

London Office, Euston Tower, 286 Euston Road, London, NW1 3DN. 071 388 1188.

Liverpool Office, Cressington House, 249 St Mary's Road, Garston, Liverpool, L19 0NF. 051 427 2061 or 051 427 6213.

Nottingham Office, Spur A, Block 5, Government Buildings, Chalfont Drive, Western Boulevard, Nottingham NG8 3RZ. 0602 293409 or 0602 293198.

7
DRUG TREATMENTS AND THEIR ALTERNATIVES

The use and abuse of psychotropic (mind-altering) drugs has been around since at least 2000 BC.

Alcohol, the most socially acceptable drug of all, was very popular amongst ancient Egyptians. Opium poppy seeds were discovered in a Swiss stone age settlement and even in 2200 BC the odd Chinese emperor was enjoying the occasional 'toot' of marijuhana.

Mind-altering drugs come in all shapes and forms. They have had songs, poems and even novels written about them. The amount of controversy and hypocrisy attached to drugs and drug taking is just as alive and well now as it was in the days of prohibition.

But one fact is indisputable. The taking of drugs for one purpose or another is an integral part of twentieth century life.

The use and abuse of drugs for non-medical purposes is discussed elsewhere in this book. This chapter looks at the use and possible abuse of psychotropic drugs prescribed in an attempt to help those suffering from mental health problems. It also discusses the damaging effects of long-term drug use and possible alternatives.

THE NEED FOR DRUGS

A drug for a physical illness, such as an antibiotic for infection, is often sought by the patient. In most instances the patient will start to feel better shortly after medication and will be grateful to the medical practitioner for prescribing the treatment. For someone experiencing extreme mental distress the drug treatment may not be welcome and may even, at times, make them feel worse.

Take, for instance, someone whose mental state makes them believe, temporarily, that people are trying to kill them. Prescribed medication may be seen as a poison and therefore be refused. The medication is designed to tackle the more distressing symptoms of the illness. But for someone who is suffering from what is termed a psychotic disorder they will be unaware that the symptoms are just that, because someone suffering from a psychosis is sometimes unable to distinguish reality from fantasy. For these people their experience of the drug, certainly initially, may well focus on the side-effects they experience.

Most, if not all, drugs developed for mental health disorders have side-effects. Many people are now aware of the problems caused by the over-zealous prescribing of minor tranquillisers over the past years. Addiction to tranquillisers is a greater problem in this country than addiction to heroin.

In an ideal world we would need little or no recourse to drugs. However, the world we live in is far from ideal, and it is often those who suffer most from this less than perfect world who suffer from mental health problems and at present, drug treatment, or chemotherapy as it is sometimes called, plays a significant part in the care of mental disorder. However, while this is a fact, and understanding drugs and their side effects is important for the self-management of mental health problems, there are alternatives as well as complementary treatments. These are considered over the next few pages (and Chapter 4 of this book).

TRANQUILLISERS

Tranquillisers are divided roughly into two main categories — 'major' and 'minor'.

Major tranquillisers (anti-psychotic or neuroleptic drugs)
Major tranquillisers are used to combat some of the most distressing symptoms of a psychotic condition — the hallucinations and delusions. These very powerful drugs can be used in the short term with an acute onset of a psychotic condition or in the long term to keep symptoms at bay so that sufferers are able to live outside hospital and, in theory, live a 'normal' life.

In the main, anti-psychotic tranquillisers are designed to combat the symptoms and not to sedate, thereby avoiding limiting people's ability to function. However, some major tranquillisers such as chlorpromazine also have a marked sedatory affect.

Although the use of drug therapy has played an important part in allowing people to live outside hospital and potentially to avoid being invalided by their symptoms, there are many criticisms that can be made of the side effects and uses of these drugs.

Anti-psychotic drugs, or major tranquillisers as they are often known, cause a wide range of side-effects. Some, such as trembling and stiffness in the muscles, can be offset by taking another medication with anti-Parkinsonian properties*. There are many unwelcome side effects of these drugs that cannot be offset by other medication, and long-term use can cause disabling side effects such as tardive dyskinesia (see p. 153), brain damage, blindness and even death in some cases.

Perhaps the greatest misuse of major tranquillisers such as chlorpromazine is to quieten the patient and relieve the

---

*Parkinson's disease causes similar symptoms to the side-effects of anti-psychotic drugs and medication that treat Parkinson's disease — orphenadrine or procyclidine — can offset some of these.

anxiety of the doctors and nurses. In mental health hospitals, the use of chlorpromazine on a PRN (as required) basis means that patients who are 'acting out' or displaying understandable distress and frustration are medicated, sometimes forcibly (under the provision of the Mental Health Act 1983), with a sedating anti-psychotic or, in many cases, a tranquillising drug such as lorazepam (see below) is used to subdue the patient.

Minor tranquillisers

Hypnotic (sleep-inducing) and anxiolytic (sedating) drugs can be used interchangeably, ie anxiolytics can be used to aid sleep, an hypnotic to calm anxiety. These drugs are used a great deal in hospitals and also prescribed (too often) in the community. Although the problem is not as widespread as it used to be, overprescribing of minor tranquillisers, mainly to women, is still in evidence.

Although these drugs can be of some benefit in the short-term, the disadvantages are dependence or addiction, withdrawal symptoms when coming off the drugs after a long period of time and tolerance to the effects of the drug, requiring larger doses. However, one of the greatest disadvantages of minor tranquillisers is that they treat the symptoms but do nothing about the causes of the problem, which might need therapy or a change in social situation or lifestyle.

DRUGS AND THEIR SIDE EFFECTS

Major tranquillisers — taken orally

Name	Sold as
Clopenthixol	Clopixol
Chlorpromazine	Largactil
Droperidol	Droleptan
Flupenthixol	Depixol
Haloperidol	Haldol, Serenace
Oxypertine	Integrin
Pericyazine	Neulactil
Perphenazine	Fentazin

Pimozide	Orap
Prochlorperazine	Stemetil, Vertigon
Promazine	Sparine
Sulpiride	Dolmatil
Trifluoperazine	Stelazine
Trifluperidol	Triperidol

Common side-effects Restlessness, tremor, stiffness, loss of facial expression, dry mouth, blurred vision, constipation, difficulty in passing water, increased appetite, faintness on suddenly standing up, sensitivity of skin to sunlight, lowering of body temperature, odd movements of body and face, increases the effect of alcohol.

The above side-effects can vary in extent depending on which drug is used and the individual person. The unpleasant effects can often be temporary.

Major tranquillisers — by injection

Name	**Sold as**
Clopenthixol	Clopixol
Fluphenthixol decanoate	Depixol
Fluphenazine decanoate	Modecate
Fluphenazine enanthate	Moditen
Fluspirilene	Redeptin

Name	**Sold as**
Haloperidol decanoate	Haldol Decanoate
Pipothiazine palmitate	Piportil Depot

The long term use of major tranquillisers (anti-psychotic drugs) include:

Acute dystonic reactions The symptoms of an acute dystonic reaction are the onset of facial grimaces or distortions, dysarthria, difficult or laboured breathing, uncontrollable muscle movements or spasms, or the eyes turning uncontrollably upward (oculogyric crisis).

This type of reaction needs to be countered by further

drug treatment in the form of an anti-Parkinson drug such as procyclidine (Kemadrin), benzotropine (Cogentin), biperiden (Akineton) or orphenadrine (Disipal).

Akithisia Agitation or 'motor restlessness' shows itself as an inability to relax.
   Again, this side effect is countered by another drug such as diazepam.

Tardive dyskinesia This extremely distressing condition can occur after prolonged treatment with an anti-psychotic drugs and might be exacerbated by stress. Symptoms are most likely to be manifest in the face but can also appear in the arms and legs. They include involuntary movements such as spasms, twitches, grasping movements, lip-sucking and jaw grating.

Parkinsonian-like   condition Because   anti-psychotic drugs act by blocking dopamine receptors, this results in a build up of dopamine as the brain tries to get this neurotransmitter through to the receptors! This causes a similar response in the body to that of Parkinson's disease. The symptoms are a physical rigidity, akinesia and tremor.

Antidepressant drugs
There are two main groups of antidepressant drugs: the cyclic antidepressants and the monoamine oxidase inhibitors (MAO inhibitors).

Cyclic antidepressants

Name	Sold as
Amitriptyline	Tryptizol
	Lentizol
Butriptyline	Evadyne
Clomipramine	Anafranil
Desipramine	Pertofran
Dothiepin	Prothiaden
Doxepin	Sinequan

Fluvoxamine	Faverin
Imipramine	Tofranil
Iprindole	Prondol
Lofepramine	Gamanil
Maprotiline	Ludiomil
Mianserin	Bolvidon, Norval
Nortriptyline	Allegron, Aventyl
Protriptyline	Concordin
Trazodone	Molipaxin
Trimipramine	Surmontil
Viloxazine	Vivalan

Common side-effects Blurred vision, constipation, difficulty in passing water, dry mouth, confusion in the elderly, increase in effect of alcohol, can aggravate symptoms in those with schizophrenia, weight gain.

MAOI antidepressants

Name	**Sold as**
Isocarboxazid	Marplan
Phenelzine	Nardil
Tranylcypromine	Parnate

Common side-effects Faintness on suddenly standing up, dangerous interactions with some other drugs, dangerous interactions with some foods (see below), increase in the effect of alcohol.

Certain foods should be avoided when taking MAOIs because the foods contain chemicals that can produce dangerous reactions if consumed with the MAOIs. The foods are any form of cheese, especially cream cheese, meat and yeast extracts such as Bovril, Marmite and Oxo, broad beans, avocado pears, pickled herrings, any food which might be 'going off'. Occasionally chocolate, yoghourt, cream and game can cause a reaction. Also proprietary cough and cold medicines should be avoided.

Minor tranquillisers

Name	Sold as
Triazolam	Halcion
Alprazolam	Xanax
Bromazepam	Lexotan
Flunitrazepam	Rohypnol
Lorazepam	Almazine, Ativan
Lormetazepam	Lormetazepam
Oxazepam	Oxanid
Temazepam	Normison
Chlordiazepoxide	Librium
Clobazam	Frisium
Clorazepate	Tranxene
Diazepam	Alupram, Atensine, Diazemuls, Stesolid, Valium
Flurazepam	Dalmane
Medazepam	Nobrium
Nitrazepam	Mogadon, Nitrados, Somnite, Unisomnia

Common side-effects Drowsiness, confusion, impaired performance on tasks like driving and working machinery, increase in effect of alcohol addiction.

Lithium treatment and its side-effects

Lithium is a salt that is naturally present in our bodies, and lithium carbonate is given to people who suffer from manic depression while they are relatively stable in an attempt to maintain a bio-chemical stability. Lithium levels in the body have to be monitored closely as too high a level can be extremely toxic. Side-effects include nausea, diarrhoea and a metallic taste in the mouth. Feeling shaky, consuming more water than normal as well as passing a greater amount of urine are matters of concern and should be reported to a doctor as soon as possible. Failure to act upon these signals which may be a warning of toxicity could result in damage to the kidneys.

ELECTROPLEXY

Electroplexy, ECT, electroconvulsive therapy — these are all names given to one of the most controversial forms of treatment available for mental health problems of a severe (usually psychotic) depressive nature.

Electroplexy is carried out, under anaesthetic and with the use of a muscle relaxant, by placing electrodes on either temple (bi-lateral approach or on one temple and forehead (unilateral approach) and passing a small electric current across the brain for approximately 4 seconds. This electric 'shock' induces a short epileptic fit. The muscle relaxant reduces the physical proportions of the fit thereby limiting the amount of physical damage a patient might otherwise sustain.

It is not known how electroplexy works and it is by no means effective in many cases. However in some instances this treatment can be lifesaving, although it is not effective in the long term. It only enables doctors and nurses to get a patient to a stage where they are able to work with them in a therapeutic nature. Also, appropriate care can avoid the need for ECT in the first place.

Although the muscle relaxant minimises the convulsion or fit that the patient experiences and the anaesthetic means that they have no memory of the treatment, patients can find the anticipation of ECT and the after effects (memory loss, headaches) extremely distressing. ECT can also be quite distressing to watch regardless of the measures taken to minimise the distress to the patient.

Patient consent or a second opinion is necessary before treatment can be given. However, patients and their relatives need to be aware of how this consent can sometimes be obtained (see Chapter 6).

Situations whereby ECT is used as a punishment, as shown in *One Flew Over the Cuckoo's Nest*, are now hopefully rare, although health professionals frustration over the slow progress made by some patients can make recourse to ECT more likely, and I have heard some (fairly unprofessional) nurses referring to patients needing 'a good zapp' ie ECT.

LEUCOTOMIES/LOBOTOMY

These are very rarely carried out. Only fifteen of these operations on the brain were performed in 1986.

ALTERNATIVE OR COMPLEMENTARY TREATMENTS

Many alternative or complementary treatments are associated with physical ailments. However, as it is not really possible to segregate the mind and body, even the physical treatments can be very therapeutic and if not holistic themselves (as some are), they can be used as part of a holistic approach to mental well-being. Although in some cases the distinction is arbitrary and can be argued, physical therapies are included in this section while psychological therapies are covered in Chapter 4.

This section describes briefly the alternatives to orthodox drug treatment and the mental health problems for which they might be helpful. There are many books available from libraries and bookshops that give much greater detail of the treatments described for those who wish to increase their knowledge and to help people pursue any alternative they might be interested in there is a Useful Addresses section at the end of the chapter.

Acupuncture

What is acupuncture? It's concerned for the mental-emotional states of people; very much concerned with nutrition. It uses in its therapeutics not only needles, but finger pressure. It uses heat in the form of moxibustion. Nowadays, they are using things like laser beams and

ultrasonics, and some people inject homeopathic remedies into acupuncture points. So there are all sorts of
ways of dealing with the energy — Chi energy.
 Joe Goodman, Ex-President of the British Acupuncture
Association

Mainly associated with alleviating pain, such as migraine,
headaches and back pain, acupuncture has also been
used as part of an holistic approach to some addictions,
such as drinking or smoking. The patient's co-operation
and will-power are essential for successful treatment.

For people who really cannot stand the thought of the
needles, acupressure, which works by locating key points
in relation to the pain or disorder and applying pressure, is
an option (see shiatsu/acupressure below).

Alexander technique
Although the Alexander technique is concerned primarily
with posture, the creator, F. Matthias Alexander, was not
concerned just with physiological (bodily) improvements,
but also with 'the restoration and maintenance of psycho-
physical efficiency and conditions of well-being'. Correct
posture can help with tiredness and listlessness as well as
preventing headaches.

Anthroposophical medicine
Based on the philosophy and teachings of Rudolph
Steiner, anthroposophy should be interpreted to mean
'awareness' of one's humanity. Awareness of one's self
(posture, gestures, etc), self-expression through music,
hydrotherapy, art therapy, all these and more may well be
employed by an anthroposophical doctor (who should
always be a qualified orthodox doctor who has undertaken
a post-graduate course in anthroposophical medicine).

This approach is very much to do with life-style rather
than taking medication for ailments.

Applied kinesiology
Sometimes known as touch for health, applied kinesiology

is based on special muscle-testing techniques which enable weaknesses to be detected and corrections to be made through touching and positioning. Correcting these weaknesses allows the bodies energies to flow unhampered. This physical therapy is good for tackling physical tensions, preventing pain and discomfort. Applied kinesiology has achieved much success in the treatment of allergies, in particular food allergies.

Aromatherapy

Aromatherapy involves the use of oils made from essences of plants. These essential oils are massaged into the skin, inhaled or used in bathing. Aromatherapists have successfully treated people suffering from depression, even long-term depression that has not responded to other types of treatment, both orthodox and non-orthodox. In fact it has been suggested that almost any disorder that might be classified as psychosomatic or stress-related may be successfully treated through aromatherapy.

Art therapy

Art therapy is used as a vehicle for expression, particularly in those situations where there may be some difficulty in expressing painful thoughts and feelings vocally.

Originally a form of occupational therapy, it was realised by psychoanalysts that people's drawings and paintings expressed what was going on in their minds. While art therapy can be used to help an individual understand themselves, it can also be useful for the off-loading of powerful emotions such as anger.

Art therapy has been used successfully in the treatment of mental health problems, such as anorexia nervosa, as well as addiction to alcohol and drugs.

Bach flower remedies

Unfortunately it is most unlikely that Bach Flower Remedies will be offered as an alternative for mental distress in any hospital, whether NHS or private.

The Bach System and Remedies were discovered and

developed by a doctor who had been a Harley Street consultant, bacteriologist and homeopath for over twenty years. The late Edward Bach, MB, BS, MRCS, LRCP, DPH, gave up a very successful practice in 1930 to work on developing remedies from the plant world which could be used to restore vitality to the sick. He was particularly interested in people who had some physical ailment and the negative thought processes that accompany illness. He believed that tackling the negative thinking would enable the sufferer to use their mental energies to assist their healing.

He discovered, in a spiritual rather than scientific manner, 38 flowers that had a positive effect upon different negative states of mind. These were:

- Agrimony — those who hide worries behind a brave face.
- Aspen — apprehension for no known reason.
- Beech — critical and intolerant of others.
- Centaury — weak willed, exploited or imposed upon.
- Cerato — those who doubt their own judgement, seek confirmation from others.
- Cherry plum — uncontrolled, irrational thoughts.
- Chestnut bud — refuses to learn by experience, continually repeats same mistakes.
- Chicory — over possessive, self-centred, clinging and over-protective, especially of loved ones.
- Clematis — inattentive, dreamy, absent-minded, mental escapism.
- Crab apple — the 'cleanser', self-disgust/detestation, ashamed of ailments.
- Elm — overwhelmed, feelings of inadequacy.
- Gentian — despondency.
- Gorse — pessimism, defeatism, feelings of 'Oh, what's the use!'
- Heather — talkative, obsessed with own troubles and experiences.
- Holly — hatred, envy, jealousy, suspicion.
- Honeysuckle — living in the past, nostalgic, home sick.

- Hornbeam — 'Monday morning' feeling, procrastination.
- Impatiens — impatience, irritability.
- Larch — lack of self-confidence, feelings of inferiority and fears of failure.
- Mimulus — fear of known things, shyness, timidity.
- Mustard — 'dark cloud' that descends, making one saddened and low for no known reason.
- Oak — normally strong/courageous, but no longer able to struggle bravely against illness and/or adversity.
- Olive — fatigued, drained of energy.
- Pine — guilt complex, blames self even for mistakes of others, always apologising.
- Red chestnut — obsessed by care and concern for others.
- Rock rose — suddenly alarmed, scared, panicky.
- Rock water — rigid minded, self-denying.
- Scleranthus — uncertainty/indecision/vacillation, fluctuating moods.
- Star of Bethlehem — for all the effects of serious news, or fright following an accident, etc.
- Sweet chestnut — utter dejection, bleak outlook.
- Vervain — over-enthusiasm, fanatical beliefs.
- Vine — dominating/inflexible/tyrannical/autocratic/arrogant, usually good leaders.
- Walnut — assists in adjustment to transition or change, eg puberty, menopause, divorce, new surroundings.
- Water violet — proud, reserved, enjoys being alone.
- White chestnut — persistent unwanted thoughts, preoccupation with some worry or episode, mental arguments.
- Wild oats — helps determine one's intended path in life.
- Wild rose — resignation, apathy.
- Willow — resentment, embitterment, 'poor old me'.
- Rescue remedy — a combination of Cherry plum, Clematis, Impatiens, Rock rose, Star of Bethlehem is an all purpose, emergency composite for effects of

anguish, examinations, shock, going to the dentist, etc. It has a comforting, calming and reassuring influence for those distressed by startling experiences.

(From a leaflet distributed by the Bach Centre — see Useful Addresses below).

For a deeper understanding and explanation of the Remedies which is important to their successful use it would be wise to read one of the many books on the subject. Dr Bach's original descriptions are in his book, *Twelve Healers*.

Colour therapy
Interest in colour therapy is growing. Interior designers are often called in by large organisations to design a colour scheme that is conducive to work in the work area and rest in the staff room.

Some hospitals are now taking account of the fact that regulation hospital green did nothing to help people get well and are using bright cheerful colours in some areas, and restful, peaceful colours in others.

While it has long been known that there are psychological reactions to colour (browns and greys can be drab and depressing for instance), the effects of artificial light as opposed to natural light is also an issue. Many people who work in environments dependent upon artificial light complain that this affects their health.

Also, research has shown that lack of sunlight can cause depression. This is now known as Seasonally Activated Depression (SAD).

Dance therapy
Dance therapy has been used in hospitals for people with mental health problems since the Second World War. It works in a variety of ways, such as facilitating the expression of emotions, releasing tension, providing some physical contact, developing and releasing energy, finding a sense of personal rhythm. It is believed that dance therapy gives a sense of bodily awareness to those who are

extremely withdrawn, such as autistic children. Attending dance classes, particularly those with therapy as an objective, can provide many benefits to people who experience mental health problems, not least helping them overcome loneliness.

Herbalism

Many, many years ago, people relied upon their instinct in order to understand which plants and herbs were safe to eat and which had healing properties. Much of this instinct has now been lost to us, drowned out by the din of expertise. However, the knowledge and use of herbs for medicinal purposes has been passed down through generations, and it was from these natural remedies that many of today's synthetic drugs were developed.

Herbalism, like many alternative treatments, has found it difficult to compete with the credibility of modern drugs. Commerce and marketing have vastly influenced the use and overuse of drugs. Multi-million pound businesses rely upon doctors taking up their products and prescribing them to patients, sometimes with disastrous results, as the section on the side-effects of psychotropic drugs in this chapter shows.

However, there is now a new interest in herbal and natural remedies, especially in the therapeutic effects of ginseng and evening primrose oil. According to Geoff Watts in an article for *World Medicine* in 1981, evening primrose oil is believed to have a positive effect on many complaints, including schizophrenia and alcoholism.

And ginseng, although still controversial, has for years been prescribed in China for depression as well as a range of other complaints. One of the difficulties in validating ginseng in clinical trials has been the fact that its efficaciousness relies not only on the individual, but on their mood at the time. However, as many doctors and nurses working in the mental health field will know, the effectiveness of potent drugs such as haloperidol, chlorpromazine and lorazepam also depend on the individual and their mood at the time. And while people who become very depressed may well need a course of antidepressants as part of a care regime to get them well, herbal remedies such as evening primrose oil and ginseng may play a useful part in keeping them well.

Other herbs associated with the alleviation of mental health problems are:

- Alcoholism — cayenne, feverfew, fringe tree, golden-seal, mother of thyme, nerve root, passion flower, quassia, redcurrant and yellow jessamine.
- Depression — sage (sometimes clary sage).
- Insomnia — anise, balm, dandelion, dill, hawthorn, mother of thyme, primrose, rosemary and many more.
- Nervous conditions (including restlessness, agitation and anxiety) — almond, balm, borage, celery, hawthorn, jasmine, nerve root, pansy, passion flower, rosemary, sage, thyme, witch hazel and many more.

Many physical conditions that might well have implications for our mental well-being can be helped with herbs. For a better understanding of herbalism, *The Herb Book* by John Lust (Bantam Books) provides a thoroughly comprehensive guide.

Hydrotherapy
The value of water as a therapeutic medium has been recognised for thousands of years. Whether used in massage, in the form of steam in turkish baths, combined with massage in thalassotherapy, taken internally or bathed in (spa waters, swimming, jacuzzi or just lying in the bath), water can make us feel good and in some cases may have other properties (minerals, heat) that make it more effective.

Ionisation therapy
Some air molecules (a few thousand out of millions) carry either positive or negative electrical charges. These are known as ions. In order for an atmosphere to be healthy, ions should be in balance or negatively charged. When there is a preponderance of positive ions, people can feel

the effects, often in the form of headaches and depression. Stormy weather, some winds, polluted air and central heating systems can all act to disturb the ion balance.

Air ionisers are available in health stores and by mail order and work by restoring the balance of positive and negative ions in the air. Research has yet to turn up any negative effects of ionisers.

Massage

Touch is very important to our mental well-being. There are a range of therapies involving touch: rolfing, physiotherapy and shiatsu are just a few. Massage is not usually seen as a therapy, although its effects can be very therapeutic.

Massage works with the soft tissues of the body, inducing relaxation through the handling of these. Massage is also therapeutic through the pleasurable warm feelings it can produce. Ideally masseurs should be skilled at building rapport with their clients. As a full body massage can take an hour, conversation with the masseur should also contribute to a feeling of well-being. Massage is more widely available than many other types of touch therapies and many masseurs are able to come to your home.

Music therapy

Most of us at some time have put on a record or tape of music we know will make us cheer up or feel sad, although music as a therapy may seem to be stretching a therapeutic point. However, as a non-verbal method of communication and expression, music has much to offer people with emotional difficulties and other forms of mental health problems.

Reflexology

The French philosopher, Rousseau, once said that the doctor's job was to keep the patient entertained until nature takes it course and healing takes place. In the same vein reflexologists believe that the body heals itself and that the therapist just acts as a mediator between you and your body's natural healing powers.

Reflexologists work with the patient's feet, identifying build-ups of crystalline deposits and massaging areas of the feet to break these up and allow them to be disposed of through the body's own waste disposal system. This allows blocked energy flows to work more freely.

Different parts of the feet relate to the energy flow to different parts of the body. The massage is often very gentle, although if deeper pressure is needed due to the nature or extent of the block some very brief but quite severe pain can be experienced.

Reflexology can be very relaxing and stress-reducing. It can also deal with a wide range of physical complaints, including constipation, diabetes, headaches, glandular disease and hypertension, all of which can have spin-off effects for our mental health.

Rolfing

Rolfing is a physical therapy that frees the mind and emotions as well as the body from past conditioning. It has as its base massage or manipulation. The focus of the manipulation is the body's connective tissue and muscle. It is in this way that rolfing differs from other manipulative therapies that concentrate on the spine.

Again, physical alignment is important. If alignment is out because of physical or emotional trauma or just bad posture, the muscles and connective tissues suffer. This in turn has a negative effect on the body and mind as a whole.

Dr Ida Rolf, the creator of rolfing, believed that our emotions cause postural change and this can be witnessed in people who are unhappy or depressed — their head is down, shoulders are rounded, chest closed in — or angry — the body is tense, rigid. By rebalancing the physical self, the emotional self is enhanced through catharsis (the release of emotional pain) and behaviour and attitudes can be changed.

Rolfers work by photographing both the front and back of the client's body before the course begins and then at the end of each session.

During the session, the rolfer uses fingertips, knuckles and sometimes elbows to free shortened connective tissue. The whole body is worked on often with an early emphasis on the legs and feet to improve the client's balance and allow them to feel more 'centred'. The majority of sessions (a course usually consists of 10 individual sessions) concentrate on individual sections of the body, while the last few are designed to realign and reintegrate the whole body.

Shiatsu/acupressure
Shiatsu is the Japanese word for 'finger pressure'. It can be seen as acupuncture without needles as it uses points along meridians or energy flows within the body. Unlike acupuncture which is rarely self-administered, shiatsu can also be a form of self-help as it is possible to apply finger pressure to accessible parts of the body.

It is often quite natural for us to do this in any case. We rub our eyes when they are tired and parts of our head and neck when we have a headache or are very tense. In fact shiatsu is very good for stress disorders.

Courses in shiatsu are becoming increasingly common and may well be offered at a local adult education centre or be advertised in the local paper.

T'ai chi
T'ai chi is a kind of meditation on the move. Using ritual movements and exercises, the emphasis is on psychological and spiritual development.

To watch, T'ai chi looks similar to a martial art in its movements, although they are slow, smooth and fluid. Both trance-like and dance-like, they induce a very deep relaxation to a point where a floating sensation can be reached. It is not difficult to imagine how restful and health promoting such a feeling must be. Again, like shiatsu, t'ai chi is becoming increasingly popular in the western world, and courses may well be offered by a local adult education centre.

USEFUL ADDRESSES

For general information on alternative remedies, you should contact the **Institute for Complementary Medicine**, 21 Portland Place, London W1N 3AF: 071-636 9543; or the **Research Council for Complementary Medicine**, Suite 1, 19a, Cavendish Square, London W1: 071-493 6930

The Bach Centre, Mount Vernon, Statwell, Wallingford, Oxon OX10 0PZ. 0491 39489.

Acupuncture

British Acupuncture Association, 34 Alderney Street, London SW18 4EU: 071 834 1012/3353.

Register of Traditional Chinese Medicine, 7a Thorndean Street, London SW18 4HE.

Traditional Acupuncture Society, 11 Grange Park, Stratford-upon-Avon, Warwickshire CV37 6XH.

International Register of Oriental Medicine, Green Hedges House, Green Hedges Avenue, East Grinstead, East Sussex RH19 1DZ: 0342 313106/7.

Hypnotherapy

Association of Qualified Curative Hypnotherapists, 10 Balaclava Road, Kings Heath, Birmingham: 021-444-5435.

National Council of Psychotherapists and Hypnotherapy Register, 1 Clovelly Road, Ealing, London W5: 081-840 3790.

Medical herbalism

General Council and Register of Consultant Herbalists, Marlborough House, Swanpool, Falmouth TR11 4HW: 0326 317321

National Institute of Medical Herbalists, 41 Hatherley Road, Winchester, Hampshire, SO22 6RR.

Reflexology

Association of Reflexologists, Slaters, 14 Willows End, London SE3 9JL: 081-852 6052.

National Institute of Reflexology, 29 Hollyfield Avenue, London N11 3BY: 071 368 0865.

INDEX

abreaction, 95
accommodation, 116–20
acupressure, 167
acupuncture, 157
acute dystonic reactions, 152
addiction, drug, 26–30, 149
additives, food, 80
addresses, 44–6, 110–14, 129–31, 145–7, 168–9
Adler, Alfred, 96
adolescence, 89
advertisements, finding therapists, 109
advocacy, 143–5
Age Concern, 117, 122
agoraphobia, 8–11
akithisia, 153
alcohol, 1–2, 11–12, 76–9, 148, 164
Alcoholics Anonymous, 105, 109
Alexander, F. Matthias, 158
Alexander technique, 158
alprazolam, 155
alternative treatments, 157–69
Alzheimer's Disease, 17–18
amitriptyline, 153
amnesia, 31
amphetamines, 28, 29
analysis, 94–6
anger, 67
anorexia nervosa, 13–14
anthroposophical medicine, 158
antidepressant drugs, 24, 153–4
anti-psychotic drugs, 150–1
anxiety, 3, 14–15; breathing and, 61; causes, 15; insomnia, 87; obsessive-compulsive disorders, 36; relaxation exercises, 62; signs and symptoms, 15; treatment, 15, 151
anxiolytic drugs, 151

applied kinesiology, 158–9
Arbours Association, 108, 119
aromatherapy, 159
art therapy, 106–7, 128, 159
assertiveness, 74–5, 100
Association of Carers, 122
Association of Community Health Councils for England and Wales, 131
Association for Group and Individual Psychotherapy, 108
asylums, 123
Ativan, 27
auditory hallucinations, 41–2
autism, 15–16
aversion therapy, 100–101

Bach flower remedies, 159–62
barbiturates, 28, 29
Beck Depression Inventory, 19–24
beer, 77–8
behaviour therapy, 100–2
benzodiazepines, 27
bingeing, 16–17
biofunctional therapy, 99
Birmingham Women's Counselling and Therapy Centre, 109
Bluhlass, Robert, 141
Bordin, E., 93–4
brain: deterioration, 17–18; stress, 62; surgery, 137–8
breathing, 60–1, 63
British Association of Psychotherapists, 108, 110
British Federation of Care Home Proprietors, 117, 120
bromazepam, 155
bulimia nervosa, 16–17, 81
BUPA, 109
butriptyline, 153

caffeine, 79
Camden Psychotherapy Unit, 108
cannabis, 28
carbon dioxide, breathing, 60–1
care homes, 117, 119–20
causes of mental distress, 4–5
chemotherapy, 148–56
children: early experiences, 49;
    hyperactivity, 30–1, 80
chlordiazepoxide, 155
chlorpromazine, 150, 151, 163
cider, 78
Citizen's Advice Bureaux, 116,
    118, 119, 120, 122
claustrophobia, 8
Cleese, John, 51
clinical psychologists, 126–7
clobazepam, 155
clomipramine, 153
clopenthixol, 152
clorazepate, 155
cocaine, 29
coffee, 79
cognitive behaviour therapy,
    100–2
Coker, Ade, 40
collective unconscious, 97
colour therapy, 162
colourings, food, 80
community care, 114–29
Compassionate Friends, 122
complementary treatments,
    157–69
conscience, 72
consent to treatment, 137–39
consumer movement, 142–5
contracts, behaviour therapy, 101
counselling, 93–4
couple counselling, 104
criticism, 72–4
CRUSE, 109, 122
crying, 61
cyclic antidepressants, 153–4

dance therapy, 162–3

day hospitals, 124
delusions, 42
dementia, 17–18
dependence, drug, 26–30
depression, 18–26; alcohol and,
    79; antidepressant drugs, 24,
    153–4; Beck Depression
    Inventory, 19–24; endogenous,
    4, 19; herbal remedies, 163–4;
    insomnia, 87; manic
    depression, 33–4; neuroses, 3;
    signs and symptoms, 19;
    sunlight and, 162; treatment,
    24–6
desenitisation, 101
desipramine, 153
diazepam, 155
diet, 79–83, 154
Disablement Resettlement
    Officers, 120
distress, 52–3
doctors, 114, 125, 126
dothiepin, 153
doxepin, 153
droperidol, 151
drugs, 90; dependence on, 26–30;
    injections, 124; legal rights to
    refuse, 139; side-effects,
    149–56; sleeping problems, 87,
    88; treatment with, 148–56

eating disorders, 13–14, 16–17, 81
ECT, 141, 156–7
elderly, accommodation, 117–18,
    119–20
Elderly Accommodation Counsel,
    118
electroconvulsive therapy, 141,
    156–7
electroplexy, 156–7
emotional blunting, 42
emotions, 89–90, 95
employment, 120–21
endogenous depression, 4, 19
environmental causes, 5

escapism, 67
eustress, 52
evening classes, 122
evening primrose oil, 163–4
exercise, 76, 83–6; and depression, 25; and insomnia, 87; motivation, 86; safety, 84–5; suitability and satisfaction, 85; suppleness, stamina and strength, 85–6; and tension, 62, 66
expression, disorder of, 42

family therapy, 103–4
fantasies, 62
feet, reflexology, 166
'fight or flight' response, 61–2
flooding, behaviour therapy, 101
fluhitrazepam, 155
flupenthixol, 151
flupenthixol decanoate, 152
fluphenazine enanthate, 152
flurazepam, 155
fluspirilene, 152
fluvoxamine, 154
food, 79–83, 154
food additives, 80
free association, 94–5
Freud, Sigmund, 94, 95, 96, 97
Friends of the Earth, 122
friendships, 121–2
Fromm, Erich, 96
fruit, 80, 81

General Medical Council, 131
genetics, 5
Gestalt therapy, 97
Gingerbread, 122
ginseng, 163, 164
glue sniffing, 29
Goodman, Joe, 158
GPs (General Practitioners), 125
Greenpeace, 122
group therapy, 102–3
Guideposts, 118

hallucinations, 41–2
hallucinogens, 28, 29
haloperidol, 151, 163
haloperidol decanoate, 152
health: mental, 50–1; physical, 76–88
health care services, 122–4
heart disease, 84
herbalism, 163–4
heroin, 27–8, 29, 149
holistic medicine, 157
homelessness, 117–18
hormones, 89
Horney, 96
hospitals: acute care, 122–4; admission to, 134–7; consent to treatment, 137–9; day hospitals, 124; discharge from, 134–5; Mental Health Act, 133–42; patients' councils, 143; post-hospital accommodation, 117–19
hostels, 118
housing, 116–20
housing associations, 117
human rights, 130–47
Huntington's Chorea, 17
hydrotherapy, 164
hyperactivity, 30–1, 80
hyperventilation, 60
hypnosis, 63–4, 66
hypnotherapy, 99
hypochondria, 31
hypothalamus, 62
hysteria, 3, 31–2

ideals, 48
imipramine, 154
implosion, behaviour therapy, 101
industrial therapists, 127–8
injections, 124
inner voice, 72
insomnia, 87–8, 164
intensive meditation, 65, 66

Inter-Cultural Therapy Centre, 109
ionisation therapy, 164–5
iprindole, 154
isocarboxazid, 154

Janov, Dr Arthur, 98
Jung, Carl Gustav, 96–7
Jungian psychotherapy, 96–7
junk food, 76, 80

kinesiology, applied, 158–9

lager, 77–8
Laing, R.D., 43
legal rights, 133–42
LeShan, Lawrence, 65
Librium, 27, 29
Life Care and Housing Trust, 119
lighting, 162
lithium, 155–6
lobotomy, 138
lofepramine, 154
lorazepam, 151, 155, 163
lormetazepam, 155
LSD, 28, 29
Lust, John, 164
Lyttle, Jack, 76

magazines, finding therapists, 109
'magic' mushrooms, 28
major tranquillisers, 150–1, 152–3
mania, 32–3
manic depression, 4, 33–4
mantras, 65
MAO inhibitors, 153–4
maprotiline, 154
marital therapy, 104–5
Marriage Guidance Council, 109
Maslow, A.H., 50
massage, 64–5, 159, 165, 166
medazepam, 155
medication see drugs
meditation, 65–6, 167
memory disorders, 17–18
menopause, 89

menstruation, 89
Mental After Care Association, 118–19
mental health, 50–1
Mental Health Act (1983), 123, 131, 132–42, 151
mental health centres, 124
mental health nurses, 125–6
Mental Health Review Tribunals, 135–6, 142
mental health rights, 130–45
mental health social workers, 127
methodone, 29
mianserin, 154
MIND, 119, 120, 121, 126
minor tranquillisers, 151–2, 155
modelling, behaviour therapy, 101
motivation, exercise, 86
muscles, relaxation, 61–2
music therapy, 165

narcotics, 29
National Confederation of Registered Residential Care Homes Association, 117, 120
National Health Service (NHS), 107, 114, 142–3
neo-Freudian analysis, 96
neuroses, 3
nitrazepam, 155
no-win situations, 48–9
noise, and insomnia, 87–8
noradrenaline, 57
nortriptyline, 154
nurses, psychiatric, 125–6

obsessive-compulsive neurosis, 3, 34–6
obsessive disorders, 34–6
occupational therapists, 127
operant conditioning, 101–2
opiates, 27–8, 148
organic foodstuffs, 81
osteoporosis, 84
overachievers, 57
overbreathing, 60

overstress, 52
oxazepam, 155
Oxfam, 122
oxygen, breathing, 60–1
oxypertine, 151

panic attacks, 8–9
paradoxical intention, 102
paranoia, 36–7
paranoid schizophrenia, 37
paraphrenia, 37
Parkinsonian-like condition, 153
Parkinson's disease, 37–8, 150, 153
Patel, Chandra, 72
Patients' Charter, 131–2
patients' councils, 143
pericyazine, 151
Perls, Frederick (Fritz), 97
perphenazine, 151
personality, and stress, 57–9
personality disorders, 4, 38–9
phenelzine, 154
phobias, 8–11
physical health, 76–88
pimozide, 152
pipothiazine palmitate, 152
primal therapy, 98
private health insurance, 109
Private Patients' Plan, 109
prochlorperazine, 152
professionals, mental health care, 124–8
promazine, 152
protriptyline, 154
psychiatric hospitals, 122–4
psychiatric nurses, 125–6
Psychiatric Rehabilitation Association, 119, 120
psychiatrists, 125, 126
psycho-sexual counselling, 105
psychoanalysis, 94–6
psychoanalytic psychotherapy, 96
psychologists, clinical, 126–7
psychopaths, 4, 38–9
psychoses, 3–4

psychosomatic illnesses, 3
psychotherapy, 90–113
psychotic depression, 19
psychotropic drugs, 148–56

Rank, 96
reactive depression, 19
Red Cross, 122
reflexology, 165–6
Relate, 109
relationships, 121–2
relaxation, 61–6, 167
Remploy, 120
Richmond Fellowship, 119, 120
rights, 130–47
Rogerian therapy, 98–9
Rogers, Carl, 91–2
Rolf, Dr Ida, 166
rolfing, 166–7
Rosenhan, D.L., 40–1
Rousseau, Jean-Jacques, 165

safety, exercise, 84–5
St Mungo Hostel and Care Services, 120–21
St Mungo Housing Scheme, 119
salt, 80
Salvation Army, 117
Samaritans, 108–9
schizophrenia, 4, 7–8, 39–44, 90
Schizophrenia Fellowship, 121
Seasonally Activated Depression (SAD), 162
sedatives, 29, 151
self-advocacy, 144–5
self-esteem, 68–74
self-help groups, 105–6
self-hypnosis, 64–5
Selye, Hans, 52
serotonin, 25
sex therapy, 105
Shelter, 117, 118
sheltered accommodation, 118
sherry, 79
shiatsu, 167
side-effects, drugs, 149–56

Skynner, Dr Robin, 51
sleep, 87–8, 164
sleeping tablets, 87, 88
social workers, 127
sociopaths, 4, 38–9
solvents, 28, 29
spirits, alcohol, 77, 78
'split personality', 39
stamina, exercise, 85–6
Steiner, Rudolf, 158
stimulants, drugs, 29
strength, exercise, 85–6
stress, 5, 51–66; causes of, 55–7;
    dealing with, 59–66; and
    imbalance, 90; self-esteem,
    68–74; signs of, 54–5; and
    tension, 66–8
stretching exercises, 61, 86
strokes, 18
sugar, 80
sulpiride, 152
sunlight, 162
super-ego, 72
suppleness, exercise, 85–6
support groups, 105–6
support networks, 121–2
support services, 114–129

t'ai chi, 167
tardive dyskinesia, 153
tartrazine, 80
Tavistock Clinic, 107–8
temazepam, 155
tension, 66–8
therapy: alternative treatments,
    157–69; drugs, 148–56;

electroplexy, 156–7;
    psychotherapy, 90–113
thought, disorder of, 42
tiredness, 87
touch, 64–5, 165
touch for health, 158–9
tranquillisers, 27, 29, 30, 149–53
tranylcypromine, 154
trazodone, 154
triazolam, 155
trifluoperazine, 152
trifluperidol, 152
trimipramine, 154

understress, 52

Valium, 27, 29
vegetables, 80, 81
Vietnam War, 48–9
viloxazine, 154
visualisation therapy, 65–6
voluntary work, 122

water filters, 81
water therapy, 164
Watts, Geoff, 163
weight charts, 82, 83
weight problems, 81–3
wine, 77, 79
withdrawal, schizophrenia, 42
Women's Counselling and
    Therapy Service, 109
work, 120–1

YMCA, 117
yoga, 66

More books from Optima

DON'T PANIC by Sue Breton

Panic attacks can ruin your life — but it lies within your power to overcome your fears. Sue Breton — clinical psychologist, researcher into panic attacks and former sufferer — shows how you can help yourself by:
- understanding what type of attack you have
- taking short-term avoiding action to suit your personal needs
- learning more about your own personality — which will give you power over panic for good.

This unique self-help method offers hope and motivation for all sufferers of panic attacks.

'This book represents a thoughtful and concerned attack against disabling fear.' Anna Raeburn

ISBN 0 356 14451 8
Price (in UK only) **£5.99**

DO-IT-YOURSELF PSYCHOTHERAPY
by Dr Martin Shepard

- Would you like to understand yourself better?
- Do you want to lead a richer, more fulfilled life?

Dr Martin Shepard draws on his long experience as a professional therapist to present this 'do-it-yourself' approach that provides a real alternative to formal psychotherapy. Each chapter focuses on one aspect of human behaviour and concludes with a series of exercises designed to give you a clearer understanding of your own thoughts and responses.

This book is extremely practical, helpful and easy to follow. It will not only enhance your enjoyment of life, but save you a fortune in therapist's fees.

ISBN 0 356 15413 0
Price (in UK only) **£4.95**

All Optima books are available at your bookshop or news-agent, or can be ordered from the following address:

Optima Books
Cash Sales Department
PO Box 11
Falmouth
Cornwall TR10 9EN

Alternatively you may fax your order to the above address.
Fax number: 0326 76423

Payments can be made as follows: Cheque, postal order (payable to Macdonald & Co (Publishers) Ltd) or by credit cards, Visa/Access. *Do not send cash or currency.*

UK customers, please send a cheque or postal order (no currency) and allow 80p for postage and packing for the first book plus 20p for each additional book up to a maximum charge of £2.00.

BFPO customers, please allow 80p for the first book plus 20p for each additional book.

Overseas customers, including Ireland, please allow £1.50 for postage and packing for the first book, £1.00 for the second book and 30p for each additional book.

NAME (Block letters) ....

ADDRESS ....

....

    I enclose my remittance for _____

    I wish to pay by Access/Visa Card

Number ☐☐☐☐☐☐☐☐☐☐☐☐☐☐☐☐☐

Card expiry date